An in-depth look at

Mathematics 7
Alberta

Class Notes

CASTLE ROCK
RESEARCH CORP

Rao, Gautam, 1961 –
  CLASS NOTES: Mathematics 7
ISBN: 978-1-77044-330-3

  1. Mathematics – Juvenile Literature. I. Title

Publisher
Gautam Rao

Contributors
Ruth Rancier
Andrea Ryan
Stephanie Vanderwielen

Published by
Castle Rock Research Corp.
2000 First & Jasper
10065 Jasper Avenue
Edmonton, AB T5J 3B1

10 9 8 7 6 5 4 3 2

CASTLE ROCK
RESEARCH CORP

Dedicated to the memory of Dr. V. S. Rao

CONTENTS

Probability

Data Analysis

OPERATIONS WITH DECIMAL NUMBERS

When you are finished this unit, you will be able to…
- solve a given problem involving the addition and subtraction of decimal numbers
- solve a given problem involving the multiplication or division of decimal numbers
- check the reasonableness of solutions using estimation
- solve a given problem that involves operations on decimals (limited to thousandths) by considering the order of operations

PREREQUISITE SKILLS AND KNOWLEDGE

Prior to starting this unit, you should be able to…
- read and write numbers to the thousandths place value
- round numbers up to the hundredths place value
- use arithmetic to solve problems involving decimal numbers
- use front-end estimation

Lesson 1 USING FRONT-END ESTIMATION

NOTES

Estimating calculations involves making a reasonable guess as to what the final answer will be. You use numbers close to the original numbers so you can work with them easily.

You should estimate in these situations:
- When an exact answer is not needed.
- When the problem can be solved by knowing about how much.
- When you want to check if an answer is reasonable.

There are many methods for estimating. **Front-end estimation** is a useful strategy that involves calculations with the first digit of each number. All the other digits of the number get replaced with a zero.

ESTIMATING SUMS

A **sum** is the result of two or more numbers being added together.

Example

Using front-end estimation, determine the approximate sum of $237 + 596$.

Solution

Step 1

Keep the first digit. Replace the other digits with zeros.

$$237 \rightarrow 200$$
$$+\,596 \rightarrow +\,500$$

Step 2

Perform the operation indicated in the question.
In this case, it is addition.

$$\begin{array}{r} 200 \\ +\,500 \\ \hline 700 \end{array}$$

The estimate is less than the actual answer because each number was decreased in value when the remaining digits were changed to zeros. Because of this, the estimate is not always as accurate as needed.

Example

Use front-end estimation to calculate the approximate sum of
2 335.45 + 43.99 +159.76 + 32.23.

Solution

Step 1

Keep the first digit of the numbers, and make all the other digits zero.
Notice digits after the decimal point are left off completely.

2 335.45	→	2 000
43.99	→	40
159.76	→	100
+ **3**2.23	→	+ 30

Step 2

Perform the operation indicated in the question.
In this case, it is addition.

```
  2 000
     40
    100
 +   30
  2 170
```

ESTIMATING DIFFERENCES

A **difference** is the result of two or more numbers being subtracted from
one another.

Example

Use front-end estimation to calculate the approximate difference of
5 490.892 – 345.67.

Solution

Step 1

Keep the first digit of the numbers, and make all the other digits zero.

5 490.892	→	5 000
– **3**45.670	→	– 300

Step 2

Perform the operation indicated in the question.
In this case, it is subtraction.

```
  5 000
 –  300
  4 700
```

The difference of 5 490.892 – 345.67 is approximately 4 700.

ESTIMATING PRODUCTS

A product is the result of two or more numbers being multiplied together.

Example

Use front-end estimation to calculate the approximate product of $1\,491.67 \times 51.03$.

Solution

Step 1
Keep the first digit. Make all the other digits zero.

$$\begin{aligned}
\mathbf{1}491.67 &\rightarrow 1\,000 \\
\times \quad \mathbf{5}1.03 &\rightarrow \times \quad 50
\end{aligned}$$

Step 2
Perform the operation indicated in the question.
In this case, it is multiplication.

$$\begin{array}{r}
1000 \\
\times \quad 50 \\
\hline
50\,000
\end{array}$$

The product of $1\,491.67 \times 51.03$ is approximately 50 000.
The estimate is less than the actual answer because both factors were decreased in value. The greater the decrease, the less accurate the answer.

ESTIMATING QUOTIENTS

A quotient is the result of one number being divided by another number.

Example

Use front-end estimation to calculate the approximate quotient of $173.42 \div 21.36$.

Solution

Step 1
Keep the first digit. Make all the other digits zero. Drop the digits after the decimal.

$$\mathbf{2}1.36 \quad \rightarrow \quad 20\overline{)100}$$
$$\uparrow$$
$$\mathbf{1}73.42$$

Step 2
Perform the operation indicated in the question.
In this case, it is division.

$$\begin{array}{r}
5 \\
20\overline{)100}
\end{array}$$

The quotient of $173.42 \div 21.36$ is approximately 5.

4

APPLICATIONS OF FRONT-END ESTIMATION

In everyday life, quick estimates are required to determine an approximate solution to a problem. For example, you may estimate the cost of two CDs and one DVD to see if you have enough money to buy all three. Your parents may estimate if there is enough gas in the car to get them where they are going. A party organizer might estimate how many people are going to attend their event in order to determine how much food to order.

When given mathematical problems, there are clues that let you know if an estimated answer or actual calculation is required. Some words that indicate estimation are *about*, *around*, *approximately*, *almost*, *close to*, and *roughly*.

Example

John collected bottles four weeks in a row to earn some extra cash for a purchase he is saving up for. He put the money in a jar on his dresser. The amounts he put in the jar were $31.75, $21.75, $12.80, and $37.26. The purchase is $89.99. Is John close to having enough money?

Solution

Step 1

Use front-end estimation.

$$
\begin{aligned}
31.75 &\rightarrow 30 \\
21.75 &\rightarrow 20 \\
12.80 &\rightarrow 10 \\
+37.25 &\rightarrow +30
\end{aligned}
$$

Step 2

Perform the operation indicated in the problem.
In this case, it is addition.

$$
\begin{aligned}
30 \\
20 \\
10 \\
+30 \\
\hline
90
\end{aligned}
$$

The estimate is $90.00. John knows the actual calculation is more than that. John has more than $90.00 saved up, which is enough for his purchase.

Lesson 2 ADDING DECIMALS

The addition equation is *addend + addend = sum.*

If you decide to buy a scarf for $12.99 and mittens for $5.99, how much money do you owe?

The problem is asking you to add the prices and find the sum of the two items.

Three strategies that can be used for adding decimals numbers are using base ten blocks, place value tables, and paper and pencil.

USING BASE TEN BLOCKS

Base ten blocks visually represent numbers. When representing decimal numbers, the value of the cube becomes 1. The blocks that follow become one-tenth smaller for each increment.

Number Value	Base Ten Block	Decimal Number Value
cube = 1 000 (thousands)		cube = 1 (ones)
flat = 100 (hundreds)		flat = 0.1 (tenths)
rod = 10 (tens)		rod = 0.01 (hundredths)
unit = 1 (ones)		unit = 0.001 (thousandths)

Example
Model the decimal number 3.142.

Solution

Step 1
Identify the base ten blocks required.
There are 3 ones, so you will need three cubes.
There is 1 tenth; you will need one flat.
There are 4 hundredths; you will need four rods.
There are 2 thousandths; you will need two units.

Step 2
Model the decimal number.

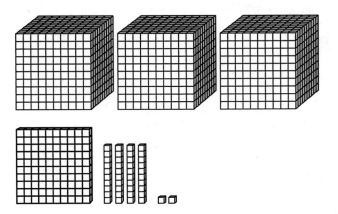

ADDING DECIMALS WITH BASE TEN BLOCKS

To add decimal numbers using base ten blocks, follow these steps:

1. Model each addend.
2. Combine like blocks together, and regroup the blocks for the most efficient set in each place value.

Example

Use base ten blocks to solve $1.73 + 2.45$.

Solution

Step 1
Model each addend.
Model 1.73.

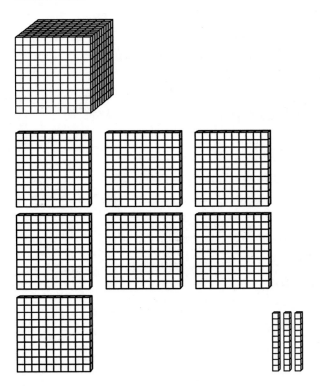

Model 2.45.

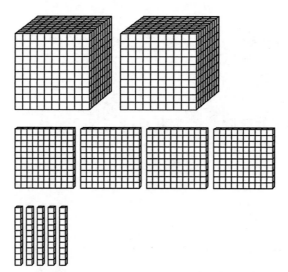

Step 2

Combine like blocks together.

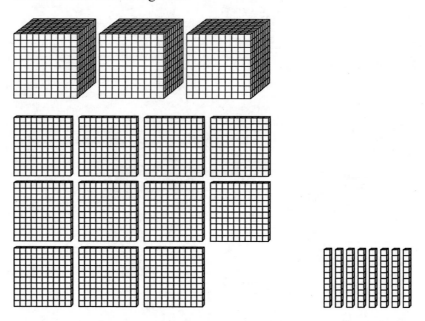

Regroup the blocks for the most efficient set in each place value.
Regroup 10 of the 11 flat blocks as a cube leaving 1 flat.

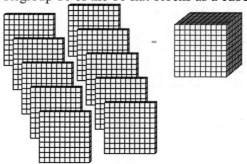

The final set becomes

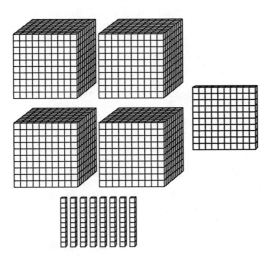

The sum of 1.73 + 2.45 is 4.18.

USING PLACE VALUE TABLES

To add decimal numbers using place value tables, follow these steps:
1. Determine the number of columns necessary, and construct the table.
2. Enter the numbers into the table. Put place holders of 0 where there are no digits.
3. Beginning from the right, add the column of numbers.

Example

Use a place value table to solve 1.73 + 2.45.

Solution

Step 1
Determine the number of columns necessary, and construct the table. The largest place value is ones, and the smallest place value is hundredths. Make a place value table that includes all three place values and a column for the decimal (four columns in all).

Ones	.	Tenths	Hundredths
	.		
	.		
	.		

Step 2
Enter the numbers into the table, making sure the decimals are lined up.

Ones	.	Tenths	Hundredths
1	.	7	3
2	.	4	5
	.		

NOTES

Step 3
Beginning at the right, add the digits in each column.

Ones	.	Tenths	Hundredths
1	.	7	3
2	.	4	5
4	.	1	8

The sum of $1.73 + 2.45$ is 4.18.

USING PAPER AND PENCIL
To add decimal numbers with pencil and paper, follow these steps:
1. Align decimal numbers in a vertical column so the digits of the same place value and decimals form a straight line.
2. Starting at the far right, add the digits in each vertical column; carry tens over to the next column. Bring down the decimal point, and align it directly below the other decimal points.

Example
Solve the expression $38.76 + 2.07 + 43.45 + 479.21$.

Solution

Step 1
Write the numbers one on top of the other, lining up the decimal points.

$$\begin{array}{r} 38.76 \\ 2.07 \\ 43.45 \\ +479.21 \\ \hline \end{array}$$

Step 2
Start at the far right, and add all the numbers in the column. Bring down the decimal point, and align it directly below the other decimal points.

$$\begin{array}{r} {\scriptstyle 1\,2\,1\;\;1} \\ 38.76 \\ 2.07 \\ 43.45 \\ {\scriptstyle 1} \\ +479.21 \\ \hline 563.49 \end{array}$$

The sum of $38.76 + 2.07 + 43.45 + 479.21$ is 563.49.

Missing spaces to the right of the decimal may be filled in with zeros as place holders.

APPLICATIONS OF ADDITION

You encounter decimal numbers in everyday situations such as shopping, measuring, weather, and time.

When solving decimal problems that involve addition, look for keywords such as *sum*, *in addition to*, *change*, *increased by*, *more than*, *plus*, *altogether*, *in total*, and *in all*.

Example

Penny goes to a ski store that is having a "Get Ready for Winter Sale." Everything in the store has no GST. The price of a scarf is $7.49, mittens are $14.99, and toques are $12.49.

a) If Penny decides to buy the scarf and toque, about how much will she spend?

Solution

Add the prices of the two items.
Often, when people shop, they will estimate the total of a purchase to make sure they have enough money when they get to the cashier.
In this case, a rough estimate is sufficient.

Use front-end estimation.

$$
\begin{array}{rcr}
12.49 & \rightarrow & 12 \\
+7.49 & \rightarrow & +\ 7 \\
\hline
 & & 19
\end{array}
$$

The estimated values are lower than the actual values. Penny needs more than $19.00 to purchase the toque and scarf.

b) If Penny decides to buy the scarf and toque, exactly how much will she spend?

Solution

Write the numbers one on top of the other, lining up the decimal. Start at the far right, and add all the numbers in the column.

$$
\begin{array}{r}
\overset{1}{12}.49 \\
+\ 7.49 \\
\hline
19.98
\end{array}
$$

Penny will spend $19.98 purchasing the scarf and toque.

Lesson 3 SUBTRACTING DECIMALS

Think:
Subtrahend is the Second number in Subtraction. Minuend Must be first.

The subtraction equation is *minuend – subtrahend = difference*.

You decide to buy the scarf and mittens. When you get to the cash register, you hand the cashier $30.00. How much change will you get back?

This problem asks you to find the difference between what you owe and how much you gave to the cashier.

Three strategies for subtracting decimals numbers are using base ten blocks, place value tables, and paper and pencil.

USING BASE TEN BLOCKS
To subtract decimal numbers using base ten blocks, follow these steps:
1. Model the minuend, and cross out the blocks representing the subtrahend.
2. Identify the quantity of the remaining base ten blocks. This value represents the difference.

Example
Use base ten blocks to solve $2.64 - 1.43$.

Solution
Step 1
Model the minuend.
Model 2.64.

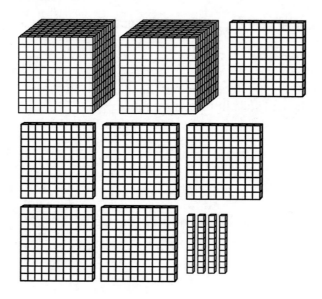

Cross out the blocks representing the subtrahend (1.43).
Start with the smallest place value, and work to the largest place value.

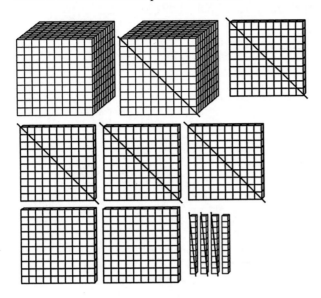

Step 2
Identify the quantity of the remaining base ten blocks.

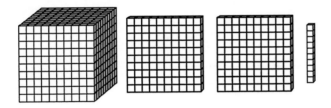

The value of the expression $2.64 - 1.43$ is 1.21.

USING PLACE VALUE TABLES
To subtract decimal numbers using place value tables follow these steps:

Step 1
Determine the number of columns and construct the table.

Step 2
Enter the numbers into the table. Put place holders of 0 where there are no digits.

Step 3
Beginning from the right and work to the left. Regroup when necessary.

Example
Use a place value table to solve $2.64 - 1.43$.

Solution
Step 1
Determine the number of columns necessary, and construct the table.

NOTES

The largest place value is ones, and the smallest place value is hundredths. Make a place value table that includes all three place values and a column for the decimal (four columns in all).

Ones	.	Tenths	Hundredths
	.		
	.		
	.		

Step 2
Enter the numbers into the table, making sure the decimals are lined up.

Ones	.	Tenths	Hundredths
2	.	6	4
1	.	4	3
	.		

Step 3
Beginning at the right, subtract the digits in each column.

Ones	.	Tenths	Hundredths
2	.	6	4
1	.	4	3
1	.	2	1

The value of the expression $2.64 - 1.43$ is 1.21.

USING PAPER AND PENCIL
To subtract decimal numbers with pencil and paper, follow these steps:
1. Align the minuend above the subtrahend in a vertical column so the digits of the same place value and decimals form a straight line.
2. Starting at the far right, subtract the digits in each vertical column; borrow from the left column if necessary. Bring down the decimal point, and align it directly below the other decimal points.

Example
Solve the expression $479.21 - 43.45$.

Solution
Step 1
Write the numbers one on top of the other, lining up the decimal points.

$$\begin{array}{r} 479.21 \\ -\ 43.45 \\ \hline \end{array}$$

Step 2
Start at the far right, and subtract all the numbers in the column. Bring down the decimal point, and align it directly below the other decimal points.

$$
\begin{array}{r}
\overset{8}{4}\overset{11}{7}\overset{}{9}.\overset{11}{2}\overset{11}{1} \\
-\ 43.\ 4\ 5 \\
\hline
435.\ 7\ 6
\end{array}
$$

The difference of $479.21 - 43.45$ is 435.76.

APPLICATIONS OF SUBTRACTION

When solving problems that involve subtraction, look for keywords such as *difference, left over, change, decreased by, less than, minus, how much more, take away,* and *how much less.*

Example

John bought a computer for $2 346.79. Three years later, he sold it for $725.00.

a) About how much money did he lose in the sale of his computer?

Solution
Use front-end estimation.
Subtract the prices of the two items.

$$
\begin{array}{rcl}
2\ 346.79 & \to & 2\ 000 \\
-\quad\ 725 & \to & -\ 700 \\
\hline
& & 1\ 300
\end{array}
$$

Since both numbers were decreased, the exact calculation will be greater than $1 300.

b) Calculate exactly how much money John lost.

Solution
Write the minuend on top of the subtrahend, lining up the decimal points.

$$
\begin{array}{r}
2\ 346.79 \\
-\ 725.00 \\
\hline
\end{array}
$$

Start at the far right, and subtract the lower digit from the upper digit in each column.

$$
\begin{array}{r}
\overset{1}{2}\ \overset{13}{3}46.79 \\
-\ 725.00 \\
\hline
1\ 621.79
\end{array}
$$

John lost $1 621.79 from the original purchase price.

Lesson 4 MULTIPLYING DECIMALS

The multiplication equation is as follows:
multiplicand (factor 1) × *multiplier* (factor 2) = *product*

When multiplying decimal numbers, follow the same process as multiplying whole numbers.

To determine where to put the decimal point in the answer, count how many digits in total are after the decimal points in the factors being multiplied. Then starting from the right, count the same number of places as the total and place the decimal point in the answer.

Place the decimal point into the answer after all the multiplication steps are completed.

Example

What is the solution to 3.5 × 2.8?

Solution

$$
\begin{array}{r}
3.5 \\
\times\ 2.8 \\
\hline
280 \\
+700 \\
\hline
980
\end{array}
$$

3.5 (1 digit behind the decimal)
× 2.8 (1 digit behind the decimal)

$980 \xrightarrow[\text{to the left}]{\text{move decimal 2 places}} 9.8$

Check the reasonableness of the solution with estimation.

$$
\begin{array}{r}
3.5 \\
\times 2.8
\end{array}
\quad \rightarrow \quad
\begin{array}{r}
3.5 \\
\times\ \ 3 \\
\hline
10.5
\end{array}
$$

For multiplying larger decimal numbers, it is easiest to use a calculator. Enter the values into the calculator along with the correct mathematical operation.

Example

Solve the expression 42.25×1.36 using a calculator.

Solution

Enter the expression into your calculator.

$$\boxed{4}\boxed{2}\boxed{.}\boxed{2}\boxed{5}\boxed{\times}\boxed{1}\boxed{.}\boxed{3}\boxed{6}\boxed{=}$$

The answer that appears on the screen will be 57.46.

APPLICATIONS OF MULTIPLYING DECIMALS

When solving problems involving the multiplication of decimals, look for keywords such as *of*, *product*, *doubled*, and *tripled*.

Systematically work through each of the steps:
Step 1
Identify the given information.

Step 2
Decide on the strategy or operation to use.

Step 3
Apply the strategy.

Step 4
Check the solution.

Example

Marie bought five books as birthday presents for five cousins. Each book cost $10.95. She left the store with $10.25. How much money did Marie start with?

Solution
Step 1
Identify the given information.

Each of the five books cost $10.95.
Marie left the store with $10.25.

Step 2
Decide on the strategy or operation to use.
To determine the amount she started with, add the cost of five books and the amount she had when she left the store.
The cost of five books can be determined by multiplying the cost of one book by 5.

Step 3
Apply the strategy.
She spent $10.95 \times 5 = \$54.75$ to buy the books.

10.95 (2 digit behind decimal)
$\times$ 5 (0 digits behind decimal)
‾‾‾‾‾
5475   —— move decimal 2 places to the left →54.75

The cost of the books was $54.75.

If Marie left with $10.25 in her pocket, she had $10.25 plus the total cost of the books to begin with.
$\$10.25 + \$54.75 = \$65.00$

Step 4
Check the solution.
$65 - 54.75 = 10.25$

Marie started with $65.00.

Lesson 5 DIVIDING DECIMALS

The division equation is *dividend ÷ divisor = quotient*.

Paige is running low on painting supplies. She visits the local art store because they are having a sale with no GST on any product. If paintbrushes cost 2 for $4.98 and watercolours cost $0.75, how many water colours can she buy with the $6.00 in her pocket?

The problem asks Paige how many $0.75 groups are in $6.00. When a number is broken into smaller parts, the operation is called division.

When dividing decimal numbers, follow these steps:

- Step 1
- If the divisor is a decimal number, move the decimal point to the right until the decimal is at the end of the divisor; move the decimal point in the dividend the same number of places.

-

- Step 2
- Divide as normal using long division until the answer either terminates or repeats.

-

- Step 3
- Place the decimal point in the answer directly over the decimal point in the dividend.

Example

What is the solution to $4.32 \div 1.2$?

Solution

Step 1

Move the decimal over one place in the divisor and dividend to get a whole number divisor.

$$1.2\overline{)4.32} \;\rightarrow\; 12\overline{)43.2}$$

Step 2

Divide using long division.

$$
\begin{array}{r}
36 \\
12\overline{)43.2} \\
-36\downarrow \\
\hline
72 \\
-72 \\
\hline
0
\end{array}
$$

Step 3
Place a decimal point directly above the decimal point in the dividend.

$$
\begin{array}{r}
3.6 \\
12\overline{)\ 43.2} \\
\underline{-36}\downarrow \\
72 \\
\underline{-72} \\
0
\end{array}
$$

Therefore, $4.32 \div 1.2 = 3.6$.

For dividing larger decimal numbers, it is easiest to use a calculator. Enter the values into a calculator along with the correct mathematical operation.

Example

Calculate the answer to $327.18 \div 4.1$ using your calculator.

Solution
Enter the expression into your calculator.

$$\boxed{3}\boxed{2}\boxed{7}\boxed{.}\boxed{1}\boxed{8}\boxed{\div}\boxed{4}\boxed{.}\boxed{1}\boxed{=}$$

The answer that will appear on the screen is 79.8.

APPLICATIONS OF DIVIDING DECIMALS

When solving problems involving the division of decimals, look for keywords such as *quotient*, *how many times*, *per*, *average*, and *each*.

Systematically work through each of the steps when solving a mathematical problem.

Example

If it costs $1.20/min to use a computer at an Internet café, how many complete minutes could Alton use the computer if he has $10.00?

Solution
Step 1
Identify the given information.
The computer use is $1.20/min.
Alton has $10.00.

Step 2
Decide on the strategy or operation to use.
Divide the total cash by 1.2.

Step 3
Apply the strategy or operation.
Make the decimal divisor a whole number before dividing.
The decimal must move the same number of places to the right in the dividend as the divisor. Add place holders to keep the decimal in its new spot if needed.

Then, follow the same process you would use to divide whole numbers.

$$\begin{array}{r} 8.33 \\ 12\overline{)100.00} \\ \underline{96} \\ 40 \\ \underline{36} \\ 40 \\ \underline{36} \\ 4 \end{array}$$

Since the remainder 4 repeats the quotient is $8.3\overline{3}$.

Step 4
Check the answer.
$8.\overline{3}$ is a repeating decimal. Take to the nearest tenth.
Doing the inverse operation is a good way to check.
$100 \div 8.3 = 12.04$
$8.3 \times 12 = 99.6$

Since a partial minute cannot be purchased, the total number of minutes that Alton can buy is 8.

Alton can use the computer for 8 minutes.

Lesson 6 USING ORDER OF OPERATIONS WITH DECIMAL NUMBERS

When solving mathematical expressions or equations with more than one operation, a set of rules called **order of operations** is followed. The operations are performed in a specific order to get the correct answer. The specific order used is called BEDMAS.

Brackets	Carry out all operations inside of the brackets first.
Exponents	Evaluate the exponents.
Division	Carry out operations in the order they appear from
Multiplication	left to right (reading order).
Addition	Carry out operations in the order they appear, from
Subtraction	left to right (reading order).

Example

Evaluate the expression $15.5 \div 2(6.1 - 2.3)$ following the order of operations.

Solution

Complete the operations inside the brackets. Within the brackets, follow the order of operations.

$$15.5 \div 2\underline{(6.1 - 2.3)}$$
$$= 15.5 \div 2(3.8)$$

Complete the multiplication and division in order from left to right.

$$\underline{15.5 \div 2}(3.8)$$
$$= \underline{7.75(3.8)}$$
$$= 29.45$$

An equal sign is placed in front of each line of the expression as the calculations progress to show that the expression that follows is equal to the expression above it.

APPLICATION OF ORDER OF OPERATIONS

The order of operations is followed when making calculations in everyday life.

NOTES

At is a keyword for multiply.

Example

Josh bought supper for his friends. He ordered one salad at $3.99, three cheeseburger combos at $5.49 each, eight ice cream sundaes at $1.29 each, and four chicken combos at $5.99 each.

a) Using the correct order of operations, write an expression for the total cost of the burgers Josh bought.

Solution

Read the problem from the beginning, and write down each number and operation as it appears in the question.
• one salad at $3.99 = 1×3.99
• three cheeseburger combos at $5.49 each = 3×5.49
• eight ice cream sundaes at $1.29 each = 8×1.29
• four chicken combos at $5.99 each = 4×5.99

Each of these individual calculations are added together to get the total bill. The expression is $3.99 + 3 \times 5.49 + 8 \times 1.29 + 4 \times 5.99$.

b) Calculate the total cost before taxes.

Solution

Follow the order of operations.
Multiply or divide in order from left to right.
$3.99 + \underline{3 \times 5.49} + 8 \times 1.29 + 4 \times 5.99$
$= 3.99 + 16.47 + \underline{8 \times 1.29} + 4 \times 5.99$
$= 3.99 + 16.47 + 10.32 + \underline{4 \times 5.99}$
$= 3.99 + 16.47 + 10.32 + 23.96$

Add and subtract in order from left to right.
$\underline{3.99 + 16.47} + 10.32 + 23.96$
$= \underline{20.46 + 10.32} + 23.96$
$= 30.78 + 23.96$
$= 54.74$

The total food bill was $54.74.

REVIEW SUMMARY

- Reading and writing numbers correctly requires a thorough understanding of place value. Decimal numbers are named according to the place value of the last digit.

- Front-end estimation uses the first digit of each number to determine an approximate answer.

- When adding and subtracting decimals without using a calculator, it is very important to line up the decimal points of each decimal number. Then add or subtract as you would for whole numbers.

- When multiplying numbers, the product will have the same number of digits to the right of the decimal point as the total number of decimal places in the numbers being multiplied together.

- When dividing decimals, move the decimal point in the divisor to the right until the decimal is at the end of it; move the decimal point in the dividend the same number of places. Then divide as normal using long division until the answer either terminates or repeats. Place the decimal point in the answer directly over the decimal point in the dividend.

- To perform questions with more than one mathematical operation, use the acronym BEDMAS. It means that operations in Brackets are done first, followed by Exponents, then Division and Multiplication in order from left to right, followed by Addition and Subtraction in order from left to right.

OPERATIONS WITH INTEGERS

When you are finished this unit, you will be able to…

- explain using concrete materials, such as integer tiles and diagrams, that the sum of opposite integers is zero
- using a number line, illustrate the results of adding or subtracting negative and positive integers
- add two given integers using concrete materials or pictorial representations, and record the process symbolically
- subtract two given integers using concrete materials or pictorial representations, and record the process symbolically
- solve problems involving the addition and subtraction of integers

PREREQUISITE SKILLS AND KNOWLEDGE

Prior to starting this unit, you should be able to…

- read and write numbers to the thousandths place value
- explain what integers are and their applications
- use arithmetic to solve problems
- use number lines

Lesson 1 INTRODUCTION TO INTEGERS

The set of **integers** contains all the positive whole numbers, negative whole numbers, and zero.

$$\{...-3, \, -2, \, -1, \, 0, \, +1, \, +2, \, +3...\}$$

An integer uses a positive (+) sign or a negative (–) sign to indicate its value. If a number does not have a sign in front of it, it is assumed to be positive. These signs represent the value of the integer. Brackets are placed around the integers to separate the integer and its sign from the operators. For example, $(+3)-(-4)$ is read as "positive three minus negative four."

A **set** refers to a group of numbers, such as natural numbers, whole numbers, or integers. Braces { } are placed around the elements in the set.

Integers represent a variety of values. For example, temperature can be +20°C or –20°C, depending on the season.

The following are some other examples of integer numbers:
- Elevation—1 000 m below sea level (–1 000 m) or 1 000 m above sea level (+1 000 m).
- Money—a profit of $10 (+$10) or a debt of $10 (–$10).

Other examples of integers are golf scores and counting down a launch lift-off.

NUMBER LINES

Number lines visually represent integers. An arrow above the number line shows the value of an integer.

The number of steps the arrow moves from zero determines the integer's value. The direction the arrow moves indicates the sign of the integer:
- A move to the right indicates a positive integer.
- A move to the left indicates a negative integer.

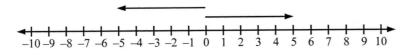

The arrows at the ends of a number line mean that the number line continues infinitely in both directions.

The arrow moving five steps to the right represents +5. The arrow moving five steps to the left represents –5.

Numbers to the right on a number line have larger values than numbers on the left, so +5 is greater than –5.

To remember whether numbers to the left or right on a number line are larger, think **left** is **less**.

NOTES

Example

Use a number line to compare the numbers +3 and +5. Then, insert a >, <, or = sign to make a true statement.

Solution

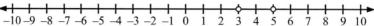

+3 is to the left of +5.
+3 is less than +5, or +5 is greater than +3.

+3 < +5

Example

Use a number line to compare the numbers +3 and –5. Then, insert a >, <, or = sign to make a true statement.

Solution

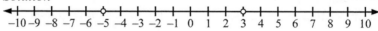

+3 is to the right of –5.
+3 is greater than –5, or –5 is less than +3.

+3 > –5

INTEGER TILES

Integer tiles can be used to represent integers. The colour of the tile indicates a positive or negative value of the integer.

Shaded tiles represent positive integers.

Unshaded tiles represent negative integers.

The number of tiles determines the integer's value.

Example

Represent the integer +2 with integer tiles.

Solution
Shaded tiles represent positive integers.
Draw two shaded tiles.

Example

Represent the integer –3 with integer tiles.

Solution
Unshaded tiles represent negative integers.
Draw three unshaded tiles.

OPPOSITE INTEGERS

Two integers that are the same distance but opposite directions from zero on a number line are **opposite integers**.

Example

Use a number line to illustrate the opposite integer for –4.

Solution
Since –4 is four steps to the left of zero, the opposite integer must have the same value and be four steps to the right of zero

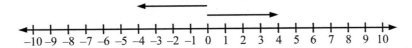

The opposite of –4 is +4 because both numbers are four steps away from 0.

ZERO PRINCIPLE

For every integer, there is always an opposite integer. The **zero principle** states that the sum of two opposite integers is always zero. For example, $(-3)+(+3)=0$.

Number lines can model the zero principle.

Sum is the answer from adding two numbers together.

Example

Use a number line to show that $(+4)+(-4)=0$.

Solution

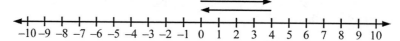

$$-10\ -9\ -8\ -7\ -6\ -5\ -4\ -3\ -2\ -1\ \ 0\ \ 1\ \ 2\ \ 3\ \ 4\ \ 5\ \ 6\ \ 7\ \ 8\ \ 9\ \ 10$$

The top arrow represents the first term in the equation. It starts at the origin and moves four steps to the right: +4. The bottom arrow starts where the first arrow left off and moves four steps to the left: –4.

A move in one direction combined with an equal move in the opposite direction results in an answer of zero because there is no change in position. The arrow ends exactly where it started.

Integer tiles can model the zero principle. When a shaded tile is paired with an unshaded tile, they cancel each other out.

These are called **zero pairs**.

Example

Use integer tiles to show that $(-4)+(+4)=0$.

Solution

Four negative integer tiles are placed first. Then, four positive integer tiles are placed beside or below them. There is one negative tile for every positive tile or four zero pairs. The tiles cancel each other out. There are no leftover tiles, meaning the sum is zero.

28

Lesson 2 ADDING INTEGERS

To add integers, there are three methods to use:
- Integer tiles
- Number lines
- Calculations using paper and pencil

USING INTEGER TILES

Example

Use integer tiles to evaluate $(+4)+(-3)$.

Solution
The first term is +4. Draw four shaded tiles.

The second term is –3. Draw three unshaded tiles. Notice the tiles are lined up opposite to each other. This makes it easy to see the zero pairs.

There are three zero pairs. One positive tile remains.
$(+4)+(-3)=(+1)$

To add integers using a number line, follow these steps:

Step 1
Draw a number line.

Step 2
Place the pencil at the value of the first term.

Step 3
Move the pencil the number of places indicated by the value of the second term. The answer to the question is located where the pencil stops.

USING NUMBER LINES

Example

Use a number line to evaluate $(+4)+(-5)$.

Solution
Step 1

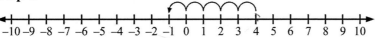

Evaluate means to find the answer.

Move the arrow to the left if the integer is negative or to the right if the integer is positive.

Step 2
Position your pencil on the first integer (+4).

Step 3
Move your pencil five places to the left of (+4). The pencil lands on (–1).
$$(+4)+(-5)=(+1)$$

USING CALCULATIONS

When adding integers using paper and pencil, there are two rules to follow:

Rule 1: If the signs are the same on the integers, add the numerical values and keep the same sign.

Example

Solve $(+3)+(+5)$.

Solution

$3+5=8$	Add the numerical values.
$(+3)+(+5)=(+8)$	Place a positive integer sign in front of the answer.

Example

Solve $(-3)+(-5)$.

Solution

$3+5=8$	Add the numerical values.
$(-3)+(-5)=(-8)$	Place a negative integer sign in front of the answer.

Rule 2: If the signs are different on the integers, subtract the smaller numerical value from the larger numerical value. Then, place the sign of the larger numerical value in front of the answer.

Example

Solve $(-8)+(+3)$.

Solution

$8-3=5$	The numerical value of –8 is 8. The numerical value of +3 is 3. Subtract 3 from 8.
–5	Since 8 is the larger numerical value, place a negative integer sign in front of the answer.
$(-8)+(+3)=(-5)$	Complete the equation.

Example

Solve $(+6)+(-4)$.

Solution

$6-4=2$	The numerical value of +6 is 6. The numerical value of –4 is 4. Subtract 4 from 6.
+2	Since +6 is a larger numerical value, place a positive integer sign in front of the answer.
$(+6)+(-4)=(+2)$	Complete the equation.

Lesson 3   SUBTRACTING INTEGERS

NOTES

To subtract integers, there are three methods to use:
- Integer tiles
- Number lines
- Calculations using paper and pencil

USING INTEGER TILES

When the integer signs are the same and the numerical value of the second term is smaller than the first term, follow these steps:

Difference is the answer from subtracting two numbers.

Step 1

Draw integer tiles to represent the first term.

Step 2

Subtract the number of tiles equal to the second term. The tiles that remain are the difference.

Example

Use integer tiles to solve the expression $(+4)-(+3)$.

Solution
Step 1
Draw four shaded tiles to represent +4.

Step 2
Subtract the number of tiles to equal the second term.

The second term is +3. Take away three shaded tiles.

There is one tile left over.

$$(+4)-(+3)=(+1)$$

For all other subtraction questions, follow these steps:
Step 1
Draw integer tiles to represent the first term.

Step 2
Add zero pairs until there are enough tiles to represent the second term.

Step 3
Subtract the tiles that represent the second term. The tiles that remain are the difference.

Example

Use integer tiles to solve the expression $(-3)-(-5)$.

Solution

In this expression, the signs are the same, but the absolute value of the second term is larger than the absolute value of the first term.

Step 1
Draw integer tiles to represent the first term.
Draw three unshaded tiles to represent –3.

Step 2
In this case there are not enough unshaded tiles to represent –5.
Add zero pairs until there are enough tiles to represent the second term.
Add two zero pairs. Now there are five unshaded tiles to represent –5.

Step 3
Subtract the tiles that represent the second term.
The second term is –5. Take away five unshaded tiles.

There are two positive tiles left over. The answer is +2.
$(-3)-(-5)=(+2)$

USING NUMBER LINES

To subtract using a number line, follow these steps:

Step 1
Place a pencil at the point representing the second term in the question.

Step 2
Move the pencil to the point representing the first term.

Step 3
Determine the length and direction of the movement. The length of the movement gives the numerical value of the answer. Movement to the right gives a positive answer, while movement to the left gives a negative answer.

NOTES

Example

Use a number line to solve the expression $(+4)-(+3)$.

Solution

Step 1

Place a pencil on the second term, +3.

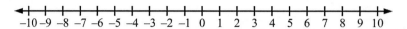

Step 2

Move the pencil to the point representing the first term, +4.

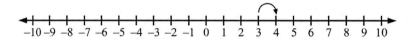

Step 3

Determine the length and direction of the movement.

The pencil moved one step to the right. This gives an answer of +1.

$$(+4)-(+3)=(+1)$$

USING CALCULATIONS

When subtracting integers using paper and pencil, change the subtraction expression into an addition expression by following these rules:

1. Change the subtraction sign to an addition sign.
2. Change the integer sign on the number that *follows the subtraction sign* to its opposite.

Once the subtraction expression has been changed into an addition expression, follow the same procedure as for adding integers.

Example

Change the following subtraction expressions into addition expressions.

a) $(+4)-(+2)$

Solution

$(+4)-(+2)$	Change the subtraction sign to an addition sign.
$\downarrow$ $(+4)+(-2)$	Change the integer sign on the number that follows the subtraction sign to its opposite. The opposite of +2 is –2.

b) $(+4)-(-2)$

Solution

$(+4)-(-2)$ $\downarrow$ $(+4)+(+2)$	Change the subtraction sign to an addition sign.
	Change the integer sign on the number that follows the subtraction sign to its opposite. The opposite of –2 is +2.

c) $(-4)-(+2)$

Solution

$(-4)-(+2)$ $\downarrow$ $(-4)+(-2)$	Change the subtraction sign to an addition sign.
	Change the integer sign on the number that follows the subtraction sign to its opposite. The opposite of +2 is –2.

d) $(-4)-(-2)$

Solution

$(-4)-(-2)$ $\downarrow$ $(-4)+(+2)$	Change the subtraction sign to an addition sign.
	Change the integer sign on the number that follows the subtraction sign to its opposite. The opposite of –2 is +2.

Lesson 4   PROBLEM SOLVING WITH INTEGERS

To translate mathematical word problems into expressions or equations, break the problem up into smaller sections and look for keywords that determine the value of all the integers in the problem. A few examples include the following:

- Positive keywords (+): above, gain, increase, up, over, more than, profit, add, greater than, larger
- Negative keywords (–): below, loss, decrease, down, under, less than, debt, minus, reduce, diminish

To solve an integer problem, follow these steps:

Step 1
Identify integer and operation keywords.

Step 2
Write an expression representing the problem.

Step 3
Solve.

Example
Lyla was given $20 and spent $11 of it. Write an addition expression that represents the statement.

Solution
Step 1
Identify integer and operation keywords.

Integer keywords: *given* indicates positive, and *spends* indicates negative.

Given $20 $\rightarrow$ (+$20)
Spends $11 $\rightarrow$ (–$11)

Step 2
Write an expression representing the problem.
$$(\$20)+(-\$11)$$

The last sentence of the problem will often indicate whether the integers should be added or subtracted. A few examples include the following:

- Addition keywords: sum, altogether, total, plus, increased by, in all, up
- Subtraction keywords: difference, change, less, decreased by, down

36

Example

A submarine was at a depth of 65 m when it ascends 21 m. What is the final depth of the submarine?

Solution

Step 1

Identify integer and operation keywords.
Integer keywords: *depth* indicates negative (–65), *ascends* indicates positive (+21).

Operation keyword: *up* indicates addition.

Step 2

Write an expression representing the problem.
The expression is $(-65)+(+21)$.

Step 3

Solve.

$$(-65)+(+21)=(-44)$$

The submarine is now at a depth of –44 m, which means 44 m below the surface of the water.

There are other strategies used to solve integer problems. Sometimes, you will need to work backward from a given amount.

Example

Janet invested in a beverage company. In the first week, her investment went up $10, then down $3, up $8, up again $4, and down $3. If she had $30 in her stock portfolio by the end of the first week, how much money did she originally invest?

Solution

Work backward by starting at $30. Do operations in reverse, adding where the stock went down and subtracting where the stock went up.
$30 + $3 – $4 – $8 + $3 – $10 = $14

Janet originally invested $14 in the beverage company.

Some problems involve adding or subtracting complex integer equations.

Example

Calculate $(-15)+(+25)+(+38)+(-23)+(-10)$.

Solution

Strategy 1

Add the positive integers (+25) + (+38) = + 63

Add the negative integers
(–15) + (–23) + (–10) = –48.

NOTES

Add sums together
$(+63) + (-48) = +15$

The sum of $(+63)$ and (-48) is $+15$.

Strategy 2

Pair up integers with other integers where their sum equals 0, cancel, and then add up the remaining integers.

$(-15) + (-10) = (-25)$

This will cancel with $+25$.

$(\cancel{-15}) + (\cancel{+25}) + (+38) + (-23) + (\cancel{-10}) = ?$
$(+38) + (-23) = (+15)$

or

$(-15) + (-23) = (-38)$

This will cancel with $+38$.

$(\cancel{-15}) + (+25) + (\cancel{+38}) + (\cancel{-23}) + (-10) = ?$
$(+25) + (-10) = (+15)$

REVIEW SUMMARY

- The sum of opposite integers is zero.
- A number line can model the addition or subtraction of integers: the length of the arrow indicates the integers value, whereas the arrows direction indicates the sign of the integer.
- When adding integers, the second arrow will move to the *right* if the second integer is positive and to the *left* if it is negative
- When subtracting integers, the second arrow will move to the *right* if the first integer is positive and to the *left* if it is negative
- Integer tiles can model the addition and subtraction of integers. The number of tiles that remain is the value of the integer, whereas the colour to of the tiles indicates the sign of the integer.
- Zero pairs are pairs of opposite coloured integer tiles that have sum of zero.
- When problem solving with integers, use a strategy to help simplify the question, and make the calculations easier.

WORKING WITH DECIMALS AND FRACTIONS

When you are finished this unit, you will be able to…
- use divisibility rules to determine if a number is divisible by 2, 3, 4, 5, 6, 9, and 10
- read and write numbers to any number of decimal places
- describe equivalent mixed numbers and improper fractions
- compare and order improper fractions, mixed numbers, and decimals to the thousandths place value
- convert all fractions and mixed numbers to decimal form
- convert from terminating decimals to fractions

PREREQUISITE SKILLS AND KNOWLEDGE

Prior to starting this unit, you should be able to…
- read and write numbers to the thousandths place value
- know what improper fractions and mixed numbers are
- compare and order numbers

Lesson 1 DIVISIBILITY RULES

Divisible means a number can be divided by another number evenly.

Divisibility rules allow you to identify if one number is divisible by another number quickly without the use of a calculator.

Divisibility rules are presented in groups because the groups of numbers have similar rules. This will help you remember the rules for the first ten numbers.

RULES FOR 2, 5, AND 10
The divisibility rules for 2, 5, and 10 are as follows:
- 2—a number is divisible by 2 if the number ends in an even digit (0, 2, 4, 6, or 8)
- 5—a number is divisible by 5 if the number ends in a 0 or 5
- 10—a number is divisible by 10 if the number ends in zero

Example

Determine if 2, 5, or 10 are factors of the number 45 672 978.

Solution
The last digit is even, so the number is divisible by 2.
The last digit is not 0 or 5, so the number is not divisible by 5 and 10.

Of the numbers 2, 5 and 10, only 2 is a factor of 45 672 978.

Example

Determine if 2, 5, and 10 are factors of the number 812 938 275.

Solution
The last digit is odd, so the number is not divisible by 2.
The last digit is 5, so the number is divisible by 5.
The last digit is not 0, so the number is not divisible by 10.

Of the numbers 2, 5, or 10, only 5 is a factor of 812 938 275.

Example

Determine if 2, 5, or 10 are factors of the number 839 729 384 190.

Solution
The last digit is even, so the number is divisible by 2.
The last digit is 0, so the number is divisible by 5 and 10.

Therefore, 2, 5, and 10 are factors of 839 729 384 190.

NOTES

Factors are numbers that are multiplied to form another number (2 and 4 are factors of 8).

RULES FOR 3 AND 9

The divisibility rules for 3 and 9 are as follows:
- 3—the sum of the digits is divisible by 3
- 9—the sum of the digits is divisible by 9

Example

Determine whether the number 876 453 is divisible by 3 or 9.

Solution

$8 + 7 + 6 + 4 + 5 + 3 = 33$	Add the digits in the number.
$3 + 3 = 6$	Add the digits of the sum again until it becomes a one digit number.
$6 \div 3 = 2$	Determine if 3 is a factor of the sum.
6 is not divisible by 9	Determine if 9 is a factor of the sum.

The number 876 453 is divisible by 3 but not 9.

Example

Determine whether the number 462 893 112 is divisible by 3 or 9.

Solution

$4 + 6 + 2 + 8 + 9 + 3 + 1 + 1 + 2 = 36$	Add the digits in the number.
$3 + 6 = 9$	Add the digits of the sum.
$9 \div 3 = 3$	Determine if 3 is a factor of the sum.
$9 \div 3 = 1$	Determine if 9 is a factor of the sum.

The number 462 893 112 is divisible by 3 and 9.

RULE FOR 6

The divisibility rule for 6 is the number is divisible by both 2 *and* 3.

Example

Determine whether the number 876 453 is divisible by 6.

Solution

The last digit is not even, so the number is not divisible by 2.

$8 + 7 + 6 + 4 + 5 + 3 = 33$
Since 3 is a factor of 33, the number is divisible by 3.

Therefore, 6 is not a factor of 876 453 because 2 is not a factor.

Example

Determine whether the number 839 729 384 192 is divisible by 6.

Solution
The last digit is even, so the number is divisible by 2.

$8 + 3 + 9 + 7 + 2 + 9 + 3 + 8 + 4 + 1 + 9 + 2 = 65$
$6 + 5 = 11$
Since 3 is not a factor of 11 the number is not divisible by 3.

Therefore, 6 is not a factor of 839 729 384 192 because 3 is not a factor.

Example

Determine whether the number 45 672 978 is divisible by 6.

Solution
The last digit is even, so the number is divisible by 2.

$4 + 5 + 6 + 7 + 2 + 9 + 7 + 8 = 48$
$4 + 8 = 12$
Since 3 is a factor of 12 the number is divisible by 3.

Therefore, 6 is a factor of 45 672 978 because 2 and 3 are factors.

RULES FOR 4 AND 8

The divisibility rules for 4 and 8 are as follows:
- 4—a number is divisible by 4 if the last two digits are divisible by 4.
- 8—a number is divisible by 8 if the last three digits are divisible by 8.

Example

Determine whether the number 823 136 947 452 is divisible by 4 or 8.

Solution
The last two digits are 52.
$52 \div 4 = 13$

The last three digits are 452.
$452 \div 8 = 56.5$

The number 823 136 947 452 is divisible by 4 but not 8.

Example

Determine whether the number 839 283 017 402 846 256 is divisible by 4 or 8.

Solution
The last two digits are 56.
$56 \div 4 = 14$

The last three digits are 256
$256 \div 8 = 32$

Therefore, 4 and 8 are factors of 839 283 017 402 846 256.

DIVIDING BY ZERO

Division by zero is an operation that has no answer. To understand this, look at the relationship between division and multiplication.

Example

Show the expression $12 \div 2$ using base ten blocks.

Solution
Draw twelve units.

⬜⬜⬜⬜⬜⬜⬜⬜⬜⬜⬜⬜

To divide, break up the units into groups of 2.

⬜⬜⬜⬜⬜⬜
⬜⬜⬜⬜⬜⬜

Since 6 groups are the result, $12 \div 2 = 6$.
Now, to show the expression $12 \div 0$ using base ten blocks, draw twelve units.

⬜⬜⬜⬜⬜⬜⬜⬜⬜⬜⬜⬜

To divide, break up the units into groups of 0. Since you cannot make zero groups, division by zero is undefined. **Undefined** means there is no answer. It is impossible to divide any number by 0.

APPLICATION OF DIVISIBILITY RULES

There are plenty of examples in everyday life when you have a total amount of something and you have to decide if it can be evenly divided.

Example

There is a shipment of water colour pencils to a school.

128 red	88 green	25 yellow
293 blue	66 orange	63 purple

a) Which pencils can be divided into groups of 2?

Solution

Any number that ends with an even digit can be divided into groups of 2.

128 red → 8 is even.	66 orange → 6 is even.
293 blue → 3 is odd.	25 yellow → 5 is odd.
88 green → 8 is even.	63 purple → 3 is odd.

The red, green, and orange pencils can be divided into groups of 2.

b) Which pencils can be divided into groups of 3?

Solution

Add the digits of the number. If the sum is a multiple of 3, then the number is divisible by 3.

red: $1 + 2 + 8 = 11$	orange: $6 + 6 = 12$
blue: $2 + 9 + 3 = 14$	yellow: $2 + 5 = 7$
green: $8 + 8 = 16$	purple: $6 + 3 = 9$

The orange and purple pencils can be divided into groups of 3.

c) Which pencils can be divided into groups of 6?

Solution

If the number is divisible by 2 and 3, it will be divisible by 6 as well. The orange pencils are divisible by 2 and 3, so they are divisible by 6 as well.

Lesson 2 USING DIVISIBILITY RULES

NOTES

The divisibility rules make sorting numbers, determining factors, and writing fractions in lowest terms much easier.

SORTING NUMBERS

Venn diagrams are visual organizers made up of at least two circles that intersect.

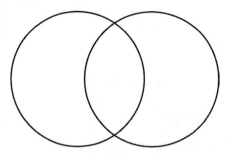

Use Venn diagrams to compare and sort information into categories based on their characteristics. If there is something that shares both characteristics, it is placed in the centre where the two circles overlap. If an item does not match any of the characteristics, it is placed outside of the Venn diagram.

Example

830, 4 837, 8 356, 847 240, 938 285, 8 372 045
Using a Venn diagram, sort the numbers that are divisible by 5 and 2.

Solution
Place the numbers that are divisible by 5, but in the left part of the circle: 938 285 and 8 372 045.

Place the number that is divisible by 2, but in the right part of the circle:
8 356.

Place the numbers that are divisible by both 5 and 2 in the centre where the circles overlap: 830 and 847 240.

Place 4837 outside the circles because it is not divisible by 5 or 2.

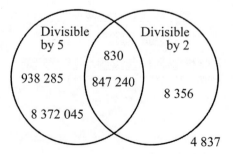

Carroll diagrams are another visual organizer made up of a table. They are more detailed than Venn diagrams because they allow for more than two characteristics to be compared at the same time.

Example

Given 830, 4 837, 8 356, 847 240, 938 285, and 8 372 045, sort the numbers that are divisible by 5 and 2.

Solution

Determine if each number is divisible by 2 or 5.

830 → divisible by 2 and 5 because the last digit is 0.

4 837 → not divisible by 2 or 5 because the last digit is odd.

8 356 → divisible by 2 because the last digit is even, and not divisible by 5 because the last digit is not a 0 or 5.

847 240 → divisible by 2 and 5 because the last digit is 0.

938 285 → not divisible by 2 because the last digit is odd, and divisible by 5 because the last digit is 5.

8 372 045 → not divisible by 2 because the last digit is odd, and divisible by 5 because the last digit is 5.

List the characteristics on the top and side of the table. Read the characteristics that are adjacent to each cell. Place the numbers within the cell that agrees with both characteristics.

	Divisible by 5	Not Divisible by 5
Not divisible by 2	938 285 8 372 045	4 837
Divisible by 2	830 847 240	8 356

DETERMINING FACTORS

Factors are numbers that are multiplied together to form another number. A number can have many factors. For example, the factors of 12 are 1, 2, 3, 4, 6, and 12. The smallest factor of any number is 1. The largest factor of any number is the number itself. Divisibility rules make finding factors quick.

Example

Determine the factors of 24.

Solution

All numbers have 1 and the number as factors.

$2 \rightarrow$ the number is even, so 24 is divisible by 2: $24 \div 2 = 12$.
$3 \rightarrow$ the digits add up to a multiple of 3: $2 + 4 = 6$. The number is divisible by 3. $24 \div 8 = 3$

$4 \rightarrow$ 24 is divisible by 4: $24 \div 4 = 6$.

$5 \rightarrow$ the number does not end in a 0 or 5, so 24 is not divisible by 5.

$6 \rightarrow$ the number is divisible by 2 and 3, so it is divisible by 6: $24 \div 6 = 4$.

6 was also determined to be a factor when looking at divisibility of 4.

$8 \rightarrow$ 24 is divisible by 8: $24 \div 8 = 3$.
8 was determined to be a factor when looking at divisibility of 3.

$9 \rightarrow$ the sum of the digits is not a multiple of 9, so 24 is not divisible by 9.

The factors of 24 are 1, 2, 3, 4, 6, 8, 12, and 24.

The greatest common factor is written as GCF.

When working with fractions, common factors are found between numbers. **Common factors** are factors that are the same in all the numbers. For example, 2 is a common factor that 4, 8, and 12 share. Some numbers share more than one common factor. For example 4, 8, and 12 have 2 and 4 as common factors. The 4 is the **greatest common factor** (GCF) because it is the largest factor that all three numbers share.

Venn and Carroll diagrams are useful for sorting the factors to find common factors and the greatest common factor.

Example

Determine the greatest common factor of 18 and 24.

Solution

Use divisibility rules to determine the factors of each number.
Factors of 18 are 1, 2, 3, 6, 9, and 18.
Factors of 24 are 1, 2, 3, 4, 6, 8, 12, and 24.

Draw the Carroll or Venn diagram and place the factors into the correct circle or cell.

	Factors of 18	Not Factors of 18
Factors of 24	1, 2, 3, 6	4, 8, 12, 24
Not Factors of 24	9, 18	

The common factors of 18 and 24 are 1, 2, 3, and 6. The greatest common factor is 6.

WRITING FRACTIONS IN LOWEST TERMS

Fractions are always written in lowest terms. A **term** is a number that is separated by an operator. Remember the line separating the numerator from the denominator is also a division sign. **Lowest terms** means the terms (numerator and denominator) have no other common factors beside 1.

To write a fraction in lowest terms, follow these steps:
Step 1
List the factors of both numbers.

Step 2
Determine the GCF that both numbers share.

Step 3
Divide both terms by the GCF.

Example

Write $\dfrac{24}{36}$ in lowest terms.

Solution
Step 1
List the factors of both numbers.
Factors of 24: 1, 2, 3, 4, 6, 8, 12, 24
Factors of 36: 1, 2, 3, 4, 6, 9, 12, 18, 36

Step 2
Determine the GCF that both numbers share.
12 is the greatest common factor.

Step 3
Divide both terms by the GCF.
$$\frac{24 \div 12}{36 \div 12} = \frac{2}{3}$$

Written in lowest terms, $\dfrac{24}{36}$ is $\dfrac{2}{3}$.

Lesson 3 CONVERTING FRACTIONS INTO DECIMALS

NOTES

Numbers are presented as decimals and fractions. To do calculations or compare the values, all the numbers in the problem must be in the same form. Changing fractions into decimals and decimals into fractions is a valuable skill.

CONVERTING FRACTIONS

Fractions can be thought of as parts of a whole. Fractions are also operations. The line dividing the numerator from the denominator is a division operator. To convert a fraction into a decimal, divide the numerator (dividend) by the denominator (divisor).

Terminating decimals are decimal numbers that come to an end. All the digits are written down. Some examples include 0.174, 3.24, and 9.819 02.

Example

Write $\frac{2}{5}$ as a decimal.

Solution
Method 1
Written calculation

$$\begin{array}{r} 0.4 \\ 5\overline{)20} \\ \underline{20} \\ 0 \end{array}$$

Method 2
Calculator
Type in $\boxed{2}\ \boxed{\div}\ \boxed{5}\ \boxed{=}$
The answer on the screen is 0.4.

Repeating decimals are decimal numbers where the numbers continue on forever, with one or more digits repeating. If one digit after the decimal repeats, it is referred to as a single-digit repeating decimal. Some examples include 0.999… and 6.634 222 22….

If more than one digit repeats, it is referred to as a multi-digit repeating decimal. Some examples include 4.125 125… and 17.080 808…

Since writing the same number or numbers over and over again is not practical or efficient, a bar is placed over the repeating digits. This is referred to as bar notation. For example, 6.634 222 22 is written $6.634\overline{2}$ and 17.080 808… is written $17.\overline{08}$.

Example

Write $\dfrac{2}{9}$ as a decimal.

Solution

Method 1

Written calculation

```
      0.222
  9) 2000
     18↓
     ──
      20
      18↓
      ──
      20
      18
      ──
       2
```

Method 2

Calculator

Type in $\boxed{2}\ \boxed{\div}\ \boxed{9}\ \boxed{=}$.

The answer on the screen is 0.222 222 222 2.

$\dfrac{2}{9}$ written as a decimal is $0.\overline{2}$.

Because repeating decimals never end, the calculator screen only shows as many places as the screen allow for. If the repeating digit is 5 or greater, the calculator will often round the last digit. For example $3.\overline{6}$ would display as 3.666 666 67.

IDENTIFYING TERMINATING OR REPEATING DECIMALS

To determine whether a fraction is equivalent to a terminating decimal or repeating decimal, look at the denominator.

The equivalent decimal terminates in these cases:
• The denominator is the prime number 2 or 5.
• The denominator is not divisible by 3.

The equivalent decimal repeats in these cases:
• The denominator is a prime number *other than* 2 or 5.
• The denominator is divisible by 3.

Example

Is $\dfrac{7}{32}$ equivalent to a terminating decimal or repeating decimal?

Solution

Use the divisibility rules to determine if 3 is a factor of 32.

$3 + 2 = 5$

32 is not divisible by 3.

Because 3 is not a factor of 32, $\dfrac{7}{32}$ is equivalent to a terminating decimal.

$\dfrac{7}{32} = 7 \div 32 = 0.218\,75$

Example

Is $\dfrac{14}{24}$ equivalent to a terminating decimal or repeating decimal?

Solution

Use the divisibility rules to determine if 3 is a factor of 24.
$2 + 4 = 6$

24 is divisible by 3.

Because 3 is a factor of 24, $\dfrac{14}{24}$ is equivalent to a repeating decimal.

$$\dfrac{14}{24} = 14 \div 24$$
$$= 0.58\overline{3}$$

Example

Is $\dfrac{8}{11}$ equivalent to a terminating decimal or repeating decimal?

Solution

The denominator is a prime number; only 1 and 11 are factors of 11.

Because the denominator is a prime number other than 2 or 5, $\dfrac{8}{11}$ is equivalent to a repeating decimal.

$$\dfrac{8}{11} = 8 \div 11$$
$$= 0.\overline{72}$$

PATTERNS WITH REPEATING DECIMALS

Fractions with denominators of 3, 9, and 11 are easy to convert into decimals using mental math if you understand the patterns.

Example

Use the fraction $\dfrac{1}{11}$ to answer the following questions.

a) Describe the pattern of the repeating decimal when the numerator is increased by one.

Solution

Convert the first few fractions into their decimal equivalents.

$$\dfrac{1}{11} = 1 \div 11 \qquad \dfrac{2}{11} = 2 \div 11 \qquad \dfrac{3}{11} = 3 \div 11$$
$$= 0.\overline{09} \qquad = 0.\overline{18} \qquad = 0.\overline{27}$$

The pattern is that as the numerator increases by 1, the decimal increases by nine hundredths repeating.

b) Predict what the decimal equivalent will be for $\dfrac{6}{11}$.

Solution

Multiply the numerator by $0.\overline{09}$.

When doing the multiplication, multiply the numbers as if there were no repeating bar. Then, place the bar over the product.

$6 \times 0.\overline{09} = 0.\overline{54}$

The decimal equivalent of $\dfrac{6}{11}$ is $0.\overline{54}$.

c) Predict what the repeating decimal equivalent will be for $\dfrac{1}{111\,111}$.

Solution

The smallest place value in the denominator is millionths. Multiply $\overline{9}$ by the place value.

$\overline{9} \times 0.000\,001 = 0.\overline{000\,009}$

The decimal equivalent of $\dfrac{1}{111\,111}$ is $0.\overline{000\,009}$.

Lesson 4 CONVERTING DECIMALS INTO FRACTIONS

Terminating and repeating decimals can be converted into proper fractions.

CONVERTING TERMINATING DECIMALS TO FRACTIONS

To represent a terminating decimal as a fraction, follow these steps:

Step 1
Determine the denominator, using the place value of the last digit.

Step 2
Determine the numerator by removing the decimal point.

Step 3
Reduce the fraction to lowest terms.

Example

Change 0.375 to a fraction in lowest terms.

Solution

Step 1
Determine the denominator, using the place value of the last digit.
Use the place value of the last digit in $0.37\underline{5}$ as the denominator of the fraction.

Since the 5 is in the thousandths position, the denominator is 1 000.

$$\frac{}{1\,000}$$

Step 2
Determine the numerator, by removing the decimal point.
Remove the decimal point. The number becomes 375.

$$\frac{375}{1\,000}$$

Step 3
Reduce the fraction to lowest terms by dividing the numerator and denominator by the GCF.

$$\frac{375}{1\,000} = \frac{375 \div 125}{1\,000 \div 125}$$
$$= \frac{3}{8}$$

Written as a fraction in lowest terms, 0.375 is $\frac{3}{8}$.

54

CONVERTING REPEATING DECIMALS TO FRACTIONS

To represent a single-digit repeating decimal as a fraction, follow these steps:

Step 1

Determine the denominator, using the number of repeating digits.

Step 2

Determine the numerator, by removing the decimal point and bar.

Step 3

Reduce the fraction to lowest terms.

Example

Express $0.\overline{6}$ as a fraction in lowest terms.

Solution

Step 1

Determine the denominator, using the number of repeating digits.
One digit repeats in $0.\overline{6}$, so the denominator is 9.

$$\frac{?}{9}$$

Step 2

Determine the numerator, by removing the decimal point and bar.
The numerator becomes 6.

$$\frac{6}{9}$$

Step 3

Reduce the fraction to lowest terms by dividing the numerator and denominator by the GCF.

$$\frac{6 \div 3}{9 \div 3} = \frac{2}{3}$$

Expressed as a fraction in lowest terms, $0.\overline{6}$ is $\frac{2}{3}$.

Example

Express $0.\overline{87}$ as a fraction in lowest terms.

Solution

Step 1

Determine the denominator, using the number of repeating digits.

Two digits repeat in $0.\overline{87}$, so the denominator is 99. $\frac{?}{99}$

Step 2

Determine the numerator, by removing the decimal point and bar. The number becomes 87. $\frac{87}{99}$

Step 3
Reduce the fraction to lowest terms by dividing the numerator and denominator by the same GCF.

$$\frac{87 \div 3}{99 \div 3} = \frac{29}{33}$$

Expressed as a fraction in lowest terms, $0.\overline{87}$ is $\frac{29}{33}$.

Example

Express $0.\overline{972}$ as a fraction in lowest terms.

Solution

Step 1
Determine the denominator.

Three digits repeats in $0.\overline{972}$, so the denominator is 999.

$$\frac{?}{999}$$

Step 2
Determine the numerator.
Remove the decimal point and bar. The number becomes 972.

$$\frac{972 \div 27}{999 \div 27} = \frac{36}{37}$$

Step 3

Expressed as a fraction in lowest terms, $0.\overline{972}$ is $\frac{36}{37}$.

If you cannot see the larger factor that both numbers share, use the largest factor you see and keep reducing. For example, the previous fraction could be reduced like this:

$$\frac{972 \div 9}{999 \div 9} = \frac{108 \div 3}{111 \div 3}$$
$$= \frac{36}{37}$$

When the single digit that repeats is the number 9 $\left(0.\overline{9}\right)$, the resulting fraction is $\frac{9}{9} = 1$.

The answer is 1 because the number that separates $0.\overline{9}$ from 1 is represented by a decimal point followed by an infinite number of zeros, followed by a one. Since that number is impossibly small, there is no practical difference between the numbers. The accepted way of expressing the value is 1.

Lesson 5 EQUIVALENT FRACTIONS

Adam has $\frac{2}{3}$ of a pizza. Samantha has $\frac{3}{4}$ of a pizza. Who has the bigger amount?

To answer the question, the fractions have to be part of the same whole. In other words, both fractions need the same denominator. To do this, make equivalent fractions.

Look at the following two diagrams. In diagram 1, two of the three rows are shaded. In diagram 2, six of nine squares are shaded. Each drawing shows the same amount shaded.

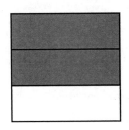 =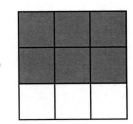

Diagram 1		Diagram 2
$\frac{2}{3}$	=	$\frac{6}{9}$

Example

Use division to create two equivalent fractions for $\frac{8}{12}$.

Solution
If the numbers are not prime, check to see if the numerator and denominator can be divided by the *same* number.

Step 1
Use divisibility rules to find factors that divide evenly into the numerator and denominator.
Factors of 8: 1, 2, 4, 8
Factors of 12: 1, 2, 3, 4, 6, 12

Step 2
Choose a common factor to divide both numbers by.
$$\frac{8 \div 2}{12 \div 2} = \frac{4}{6}$$

Step 3
Choose another common factor to divide both numbers by.
$$\frac{8 \div 4}{12 \div 4} = \frac{2}{3}$$

The fractions $\frac{2}{3}$ and $\frac{4}{6}$ are equivalent to $\frac{8}{12}$.

To make an equivalent fraction, it does not have to be the GCF. Only when reducing to lowest terms does the GCF have to be used.

The GCF is 4.
The fraction $\frac{2}{3}$ is an equivalent fraction in lowest terms.

Example

Use multiplication to create two equivalent fractions for $\dfrac{3}{4}$.

Solution

Choose any number to be the factor. Multiply the numerator and denominator by the factor.

$$\frac{3 \times 3}{4 \times 3} = \frac{9}{12}$$

Multiply the numerator and denominator by another factor.

$$\frac{3 \times 4}{4 \times 4} = \frac{12}{16}$$

The fractions $\dfrac{9}{12}$ and $\dfrac{12}{16}$ are equivalent to $\dfrac{3}{4}$.

COMPARING USING EQUIVALENT FRACTIONS

To make equivalent fractions with two or more fractions, follow these steps:

Step 1

Find the lowest common denominator (LCD) of both fractions.

Step 2

Multiply or divide the numerator and denominator by the same factor.

Step 3

Compare the numerators.

Example

$$\frac{2}{3} \bigcirc \frac{3}{4}$$

Insert a >, <, or = sign to make the statement true.

Solution

Before comparing the fractions, they have to be rewritten as equivalent fractions with the same denominator.

Step 1

Find the LCD.

List the multiples of both denominators until a common multiple appears.
3: 3, 6, 9, <u>12</u>
4: 4, 8, <u>12</u>

The LCD of 3 and 4 is 12.

Step 2
Multiply the numerator and denominator of the first fraction by 4 to create an equivalent fraction with a denominator of 12.

$$\frac{2 \times 4}{3 \times 4} = \frac{8}{12}$$

Multiply the numerator and denominator of the second fraction by 3 to create an equivalent fraction with a denominator of 12.

$$\frac{3 \times 3}{4 \times 3} = \frac{9}{12}$$

Step 3
Compare the numerators to determine the larger fraction.

$$\frac{8}{12} < \frac{9}{12}$$

Since 8 is smaller than 9, $\frac{2}{3} < \frac{3}{4}$.

Link the equivalent fraction to its original fraction.

The divisibility rules can be used to determine whether the denominator of one fraction is a multiple of the other fraction.

Example

$\frac{2}{4} \bigcirc \frac{3}{8}$ Insert a >, <, or = sign to make the statement true.

Solution
Step 1
Find the LCD.

Use divisibility rules to determine if the smaller denominator (4) is a factor of the larger denominator (8).
8 is divisible by 4.

Step 2
Because 4 is a factor of 8, multiply the numerator and denominator of $\frac{2}{4}$, by 2 to create an equivalent fraction with a denominator of 8.

$$\frac{2 \times 2}{4 \times 2} = \frac{4}{8}$$

Step 3
Compare the numerators.

$$\frac{4}{8} > \frac{3}{8}$$

Since 4 is larger than 3, $\frac{2}{4} > \frac{3}{8}$.

To compare the value of mixed numbers, look at the whole number first. If the whole numbers of the mixed numbers are *different*, compare their values to determine the larger or smaller mixed number.

Example

$$3\frac{2}{3} \bigcirc 5\frac{1}{2}$$

Insert a >, <, or = sign to make the statement true.

Solution

The whole numbers are different (3 and 5). Since 5 is the larger value, $3\frac{2}{3} < 5\frac{1}{2}$.

If the whole numbers are the *same*, make equivalent fractions of the fraction part of the mixed number.

Example

$$5\frac{2}{5} \bigcirc 5\frac{2}{4}$$

Insert a >, <, or = sign to make the statement true.

Solution

The whole numbers are the same. Make equivalent fractions of the fraction part of the mixed number.

Step 1

Find the LCD.

List the multiples of both denominators until a common multiple appears.

5: 5, 10, 15, <u>20</u>

4: 4, 8, 12, 16, <u>20</u>

The LCD of 5 and 4 is 20.

Step 2

Multiply the numerator and denominator of the first fraction by 4 to create an equivalent fraction with a denominator of 20.

$$\frac{2 \times 4}{5 \times 4} = \frac{8}{20}$$

Multiply the numerator and denominator by 5 to create an equivalent fraction with a denominator of 20.

$$\frac{2 \times 5}{4 \times 5} = \frac{10}{20}$$

Step 3

Compare the numerators to determine the larger fraction.

$$\frac{8}{20} < \frac{10}{20}$$

Since 8 is smaller than 10, $5\frac{2}{5} < 5\frac{2}{4}$.

60

APPLICATION OF EQUIVALENT FRACTIONS

There are times when quantities are given in fraction form with different denominators.

Example

Jimmy, Priya, and Ali were all working on homework assignments. Jimmy completed $\dfrac{5}{6}$ of his homework assignment, Priya completed $\dfrac{2}{3}$ of her assignment, and Ali completed $\dfrac{3}{5}$ of his assignment. Who completed the **most** homework?

Solution

Step 1

Determine what the problem is asking.

The problem is asking for the person who completed the most homework.

Step 2

Determine the given information.

Jimmy completed $\dfrac{5}{6}$.

Priya completed $\dfrac{2}{3}$.

Ali completed $\dfrac{3}{5}$.

Step 3

Identify the strategy or operation to use.

Strategy: equivalent fractions

Step 4

Apply the strategy or operation.

Multiples of 6: 6, 12, 18, 24, <u>30</u>
Multiples of 3: 3, 6, 9, 12, 15, 18, 21, 24, 27, <u>30</u>
Multiples of 5: 5, 10, 15, 20, 25, <u>30</u>

$$\frac{5\times 5}{6\times 5}=\frac{25}{30} \qquad \frac{2\times 10}{3\times 10}=\frac{20}{30} \qquad \frac{3\times 6}{5\times 6}=\frac{18}{30}$$

The largest numerator is 25. $\dfrac{25}{30}=\dfrac{5}{6}$ is the biggest faction.

Jimmy completed the most homework.

Lesson 6 COMPARING AND ORDERING NUMBERS

The following are three strategies used to compare fractions, decimals, and whole numbers:

- Benchmarks
- Place value tables
- Equivalent fractions

USING BENCHMARKS

A benchmark is a reference point used to judge the location of another value on a number line.

Divisions in the number line can include fractions. Four commonly used benchmark fractions are $\dfrac{1}{10}$, $\dfrac{1}{4}$, $\dfrac{1}{2}$, and $\dfrac{3}{4}$.

Memorizing the benchmark fractions and their decimal equivalents allows you to compare fractions and decimals without converting their formats.

Fraction	Decimal
$\dfrac{1}{10}$	0.10
$\dfrac{1}{4}$	0.25
$\dfrac{1}{2}$	0.50
$\dfrac{3}{4}$	0.75

To order numbers using benchmarks, first order the numbers greater than 1 and then order the numbers less than 1.

Example

$$0.3, \frac{5}{2}, 1\frac{1}{4}, \frac{1}{5}, \frac{3}{9}, 2.25, \frac{2}{5}, \frac{3}{12}$$

Descending means from largest to smallest.

Using benchmarks on a number line, order the set of numbers in descending order.

Solution

Start with the numbers greater than 1: $\dfrac{5}{2}$, $1\dfrac{1}{4}$, and 2.25.

Convert the improper fraction $\dfrac{5}{2}$ to a mixed number.

$$5 \div 2 = 2 \text{ R1}$$
$$= 2\frac{1}{2}$$

The three numbers greater than 1 are $2\frac{1}{2}$, $1\frac{1}{4}$, and 2.25.

Compare the whole numbers. The number 1 is smaller than the other two whole numbers. The fraction falls on a benchmark.

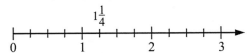

Look at the decimal and fraction of the two remaining numbers: $2\frac{1}{2}$ and 2.25. The benchmark equivalents show that $0.25 = \frac{1}{4}$ is less than $\frac{1}{2} = 0.50$.

The remaining numbers are 0.3, $\frac{1}{5}$, $\frac{3}{9}$, $\frac{2}{5}$, and $\frac{3}{12}$.

Look for fractions that can be reduced to lowest terms. The fractions $\frac{3}{9}$ and $\frac{3}{12}$ can both be reduced.

$$\frac{3 \div 3}{9 \div 3} = \frac{1}{3} \qquad \frac{3 \div 3}{12 \div 3} = \frac{1}{4}$$

When the numerators are the same, the fraction with the *smallest* denominator is the *largest*. Using the reduced fractions, there are three fractions with the same numerator: $\frac{1}{5}$, $\frac{1}{3}$, and $\frac{1}{4}$. Evaluate them based on their denominators and their position relative to the benchmark.

The fraction $\frac{1}{4}$ is a benchmark and placed automatically.

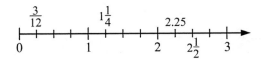

The denominator 3 is smaller than the denominator 4, so $\frac{1}{3}$ is larger than $\frac{1}{4}$.

The denominator 5 is larger than the denominator 4. $\frac{1}{5}$ is smaller than $\frac{1}{4}$.

Only 0.3 and $\frac{2}{5}$ remain. Recall that $\frac{1}{3}$ is a repeating decimal that equals $0.\overline{3}$. $\frac{1}{3}$ is slightly larger than 0.3.

$\frac{2}{5}$ has the same denominator as $\frac{1}{5}$. The numerator 2 is greater than the numerator 1, so $\frac{2}{5}$ is to the right of $\frac{1}{5}$ on the number line.

Use equivalent decimals.

$$\frac{2}{5} = 2 \div 5$$
$$= 0.4$$

The number 0.4 is greater than 0.3 and $0.\overline{3}$, but less than $\frac{1}{2} = 0.5$.

Written in descending order, the fractions are $\frac{5}{2}$, 2.25, $1\frac{1}{4}$, $\frac{2}{5}$, $\frac{3}{9}$, 0.3, $\frac{3}{12}$, and $\frac{1}{5}$.

USING PLACE VALUE TABLES

To order numbers using place value tables, follow these steps:

Step 1

Change all fractions to their decimal equivalents.

Step 2

In a place value table, rank each decimal number based on its place value.

Example

Use a place value table to order 0.3, $\dfrac{5}{2}$, $1\dfrac{1}{4}$, $\dfrac{1}{5}$, $\dfrac{3}{9}$, 2.25, $\dfrac{2}{5}$, and $\dfrac{3}{12}$ in ascending order.

Solution

Step 1

Change all fractions to their decimal equivalents.

$\dfrac{5}{2} = 2.5$	$1\dfrac{1}{4} = 1.25$
$\dfrac{1}{5} = 0.2$	$\dfrac{3}{9} = 0.\overline{3}$
$\dfrac{2}{5} = 0.4$	$\dfrac{3}{12} = 0.25$

Step 2

In a place value table, rank each decimal number based on its place value.

Ones	.	Tenths	Hundredths	Thousandths	Rank
0	.	3	0	0	
2	.	5	0	0	
1	.	2	5	0	
0	.	2	0	0	
0	.	3	3	3	
2	.	2	5	0	
0	.	4	0	0	
0	.	2	5	0	

Ascending means smallest to largest.

Start by evaluating the numbers less than 1. Look at the numbers with a 0 in the ones place. Compare the tenths place.

The smallest value is 2 tenths. There are two numbers with a 2 in the tenths place. Move to the hundredths position. Since 0 is smaller than 5, 0.2 is smaller than 0.25.

Ones	.	Tenths	Hundredths	Thousandths	Rank
0	.	3	0	0	
2	.	5	0	0	
1	.	2	5	0	
0	.	2	0	0	1
0	.	3	3	3	
2	.	2	5	0	
0	.	4	0	0	
0	.	2	5	0	2

There are two numbers with 3 in the tenths place. Move to the hundredths place. Since 0 is smaller than 3, 0.3 is smaller than $0.\overline{3}$.

Ones	.	Tenths	Hundredths	Thousandths	Rank
0	.	3	0	0	3
2	.	5	0	0	
1	.	2	5	0	
0	.	2	0	0	1
0	.	3	3	3	4
2	.	2	5	0	
0	.	4	0	0	
0	.	2	5	0	2

There is only one more number less than 1.

Ones	.	Tenths	Hundredths	Thousandths	Rank
0	.	3	0	0	3
2	.	5	0	0	
1	.	2	5	0	
0	.	2	0	0	1
0	.	3	3	3	4
2	.	2	5	0	
0	.	4	0	0	5
0	.	2	5	0	2

Look at the ones place. Since 1 is smaller than 2, 1.25 is the next smallest number.

Ones	.	Tenths	Hundredths	Thousandths	Rank
0	.	3	0	0	3
2	.	5	0	0	
1	.	2	5	0	6
0	.	2	0	0	1
0	.	3	3	3	4
2	.	2	5	0	
0	.	4	0	0	5
0	.	2	5	0	2

There are two numbers with 2 in the ones places. Move to the tenths place. Since 2 is less than 5, 2.25 is smaller than 2.5.

Ones	.	Tenths	Hundredths	Thousandths	Rank
0	.	3	0	0	3
2	.	5	0	0	8
1	.	2	5	0	6
0	.	2	0	0	1
0	.	3	3	3	4
2	.	2	5	0	7
0	.	4	0	0	5
0	.	2	5	0	2

Written in ascending order, the numbers are $\frac{1}{5}$, $\frac{3}{12}$, 0.3, $\frac{3}{9}$, $\frac{2}{5}$, $1\frac{1}{4}$, 2.25, and $\frac{5}{2}$.

USING EQUIVALENT FRACTIONS

If most of the denominators are the same, it is easiest to make equivalent fractions with the ones that have different denominators.

Example

Using equivalent fractions, order 0.8, $\dfrac{12}{5}$, $1\dfrac{1}{5}$, $\dfrac{3}{5}$, 2.2, $\dfrac{2}{5}$, and $\dfrac{2}{10}$ from largest to smallest.

Solution

Step 1

Convert the decimals to fractions in lowest terms.

$$2.2 = 2\dfrac{2}{10}$$

$$0.8 = \dfrac{8 \div 2}{10 \div 2} \qquad = \dfrac{2 \times 10 + 2}{10}$$

$$= \dfrac{4}{5} \qquad\qquad = \dfrac{22 \div 2}{10 \div 2}$$

$$= \dfrac{11}{5}$$

Step 2

Change mixed numbers into improper fractions.

$$1\dfrac{1}{5} = \dfrac{1 \times 5 + 1}{5}$$

$$= \dfrac{6}{5}$$

Step 3

Make equivalent fractions of those without a denominator of 5.

$$\dfrac{2}{10} = \dfrac{2 \div 2}{10 \div 5}$$

$$= \dfrac{1}{5}$$

Step 4

Compare the numerators.

$$\dfrac{4}{5}, \dfrac{12}{5}, \dfrac{6}{5}, \dfrac{3}{5}, \dfrac{11}{5}, \dfrac{2}{5}, \dfrac{1}{5}$$

The numbers from largest to smallest are $\dfrac{12}{5}$, 2.2, $1\dfrac{1}{5}$, 0.8, $\dfrac{3}{5}$, $\dfrac{2}{5}$, and $\dfrac{2}{10}$.

REVIEW SUMMARY

- A number is divisible by
  - 2 if the number ends in an even digit (0, 2, 4, 6, or 8)
  - 3 if the sum of the digits is divisible by 3
  - 4 if the last two digits are divisible by 4
  - 5 if the number ends in a 0 or 5
  - 6 if the number is divisible by 2 and 3
  - 8 if the last three digits are divisible by 8
  - 9 if the sum of the digits is divisible by 9
  - 10 if the number ends in zero
- Division by zero is an operation that has no answer.
- Venn diagrams are used to compare and sort information into categories based on their characteristics. If there is something that shares both characteristics, it is placed in the centre where the two circles overlap. If an item does not match any of the characteristics, it is placed outside of the Venn diagram.
- Carroll diagrams are more detailed than Venn diagrams because they allow for more than two characteristics to be compared at the same time.
- Common factors are factors that are the same in all the numbers being compared. The greatest common factor (GCF) is the largest factor that all the numbers being compared share.
- To convert a fraction to a decimal, divide the numerator (dividend) by the denominator (divisor).
- A benchmark is a reference point used to judge the location of another number on a number line. Divisions in the number line can include whole numbers or fractions.

WORKING WITH PERCENTS

When you are finished this unit, you will be able to…
- estimate and calculate percentages
- convert between fractions, decimals, and percentages
- estimate the answer to problems that involve whole numbers and decimals

PREREQUISITE SKILLS AND KNOWLEDGE

Prior to starting this unit, you should be able to…
- read and write numbers to the thousandths place value
- know what percent is
- round numbers up to the hundredths place value
- demonstrate your understanding of decimals and their place value

Lesson 1 EXPRESSING PERCENTAGES AS FRACTIONS AND DECIMALS

Percent means *"for every 100."*

Percents are written using the percent symbol, %.

40% means *for every 40 out of 100.*

Percents can be expressed as fractions and decimals.

CONVERTING PERCENTAGES INTO FRACTIONS

Fractions are comprised of a numerator that represents the part and a denominator that represents the whole.

A percentage represents a part of a whole, where the whole is 100.

Because a percentage is a number out of 100, they can be expressed as fractions where the denominator is 100.

For example, $85\% = \dfrac{85}{100} \rightarrow 85$ out of 100

Example
Convert 25% into a fraction.

> *Solution*
> **Step 1**
> Write the percentage over a denominator of 100.
>
> 25% means 25 out of 100, so it can be written as $\dfrac{25}{100}$.
>
> **Step 2**
> Simplify the fraction.
> Divide the numerator and the denominator by 25.
> $$\dfrac{25 \div 25}{100 \div 25} = \dfrac{1}{4}$$
>
> Therefore, 25% can be written as $\dfrac{1}{4}$.

CONVERTING PERCENTAGES INTO DECIMAL NUMBERS
A percentage can also be converted into a decimal number. To change a percent into a decimal, move the decimal point in the percentage two places to the left and remove the percent symbol.

Example

Change 25% into a decimal.

Solution

Move the decimal point two places to the left and remove the percent symbol.

$25\% \rightarrow 25. \rightarrow 0.25$

Therefore, 25% can be written as 0.25.

PROBLEM SOLVING WITH PERCENTAGES

When solving problems involving finding percentages, you could be required to identify a fraction or decimal before you can calculate the percentage.

To calculate the percentage, follow these steps:

Step 1
Identify the fraction.

Step 2
Calculate the decimal equivalent of the fraction.

Step 3
Write the percentage.

Unless otherwise stated, round the percentage to the nearest whole number.

Example

Harvey has a monthly salary of $3 600. He spends $580 per month on food. What percentage of his monthly salary does he spend on food?

Solution

Step 1
Identify the fraction.
The amount spent on food represents the part which is 580.
The entire monthly salary represents the whole which is 3 600.
The fraction is $\dfrac{580}{3\ 600}$.

Step 2
Calculate the decimal equivalent of the fraction.
Divide the numerator by the denominator.
$580 \div 3\ 600 \doteq 0.16$

Step 3
Write the percentage.
Multiply the result by 100, and place a percent symbol after the answer.
$0.16 \times 100 = 16\%$

Harvey spends approximately 16% of his monthly salary on food.

Sometimes when you go shopping, there are signs indicating a bonus on some items. For example, you may see a bottle of shampoo with a label saying "100 mL for free." It is helpful to know the percentage increase or decrease so you can determine if it is a good deal.

Use the same steps to calculate the percentage.

Example

The original price of a shirt was $50, and it was put on sale for $30.
The original price of another shirt was $75 and is now on sale for $50.
Which shirt is the better deal?

Solution

Step 1
Determine the fraction.
The decrease in price is the numerator, and the original price is the denominator.
The decrease in price of the first shirt is $50 - 30 = 20$.
The original price of the first shirt was $50.

The fraction is $\dfrac{20}{50}$.

The decrease in the price of the second shirt is $75 - 50 = 25$.
The original price of the second shirt was $75.

The fraction is $\dfrac{25}{75}$.

Step 2
Calculate the decimal equivalent of the fractions.
Divide the numerator by the denominator.
First shirt: $20 \div 50 = 0.40$
Second shirt: $25 \div 75 \doteq 0.33$

Step 3
Write the percentage.
Multiply the result by 100, and place a percent sign after the answer.
First shirt: $0.40 \times 100 = 40\%$
Second shirt: $0.33 \times 100 = 33\%$

The first shirt has the greater percentage of decrease, which means it is the better deal.

Lesson 2   PERCENT OF A NUMBER

A sign in the department store says shoes are 20% off the regular price. If the shoes are regularly $120.00, what is the discount?

The question is asking you to calculate the percent, or part of, a number. What is 20% of 120?

The two methods used to find the percent of a number are: equivalent fractions and multiplying by a decimal.

USING EQUIVALENT FRACTIONS

To calculate the percent of a number using equivalent fractions, follow these steps:

Step 1
Set up equivalent fractions with the percentage being the first fraction.

Step 2
Determine how the equivalent denominator was created.

Step 3
Multiply or divide the numerator by the same number.

Example
Using equivalent fractions, find 18% of 200.

Solution
Step 1
Set up equivalent fractions.

Write the percentage as the first fraction. The numerator of the second fraction is represented with a variable (a letter or symbol used to represent a value). The denominator is the given number.

$$\frac{18}{100} = \frac{x}{200}$$

Step 2
Determine the number used to create the equivalent denominator.

The denominator is multiplied by 2 to get 200.
$$100 \times 2 = 200$$

Step 3
Multiply the numerator by the same number.

$$\frac{18 \times 2}{100 \times 2} = \frac{36}{200}$$

18% of 200 is 36.

MULTIPLYING BY A DECIMAL

To calculate the percent of a number by multiplying by a decimal, follow these steps:

Step 1
Convert the percentage into a decimal.

Step 2
Multiply the decimal number by the given number.

Example

Calculate 18% of 200.

Solution

Step 1
Convert the percentage to a decimal.
$18\% = 0.18$

Step 2
Multiply the decimal number by the given number.
$0.18 \times 200 = 36$

18% of 200 is 36.

FINDING THE VALUE OF THE UNKNOWN NUMBER

Sometimes, the denominator is the unknown value. In this case, only the equivalent fraction strategy will allow you to calculate the unknown value.

Example

5 is 25% of what number?

Solution

Step 1
Set up equivalent fractions.
The percent is written as the first fraction.
Since 5 represents the part, it will go in the numerator of the second fraction.

$$\frac{25}{100} = \frac{5}{x}$$

Step 2
Determine the number used to create the equivalent numerator.
The numerator is divided by 5 to get 5.
$25 \div 5 = 5$

Step 3
Divide the denominator by the same divisor.

$$\frac{25 \div 5}{100 \div 5} = \frac{5}{20}$$

5 is 25% of 20.

REVIEW SUMMARY

- Percent means out of 100. The percent sign (%) behind a number is used to indicate that the number is a percentage.
- To convert a percentage into a fraction, place the percent as the numerator and 100 as the denominator.
- To convert a percentage into a decimal number, move the decimal in the percent two places to the left and remove the percent symbol.
- To calculate a percent of a number use equivalent fractions.
- To calculate a percent of a number, convert the percentage to a decimal and multiply by the decimal.

FRACTION OPERATIONS

When you are finished this unit, you will be able to…

- determine the common denominator of a given set of positive fractions or mixed numbers
- simplify a given positive fraction or mixed number by identifying the common factor between the numerator and denominator
- determine the sum of two given positive fractions with like and unlike denominators
- determine the difference of two given positive fractions with like and unlike denominators
- determine the sum of two mixed numbers with like and unlike denominators
- determine the difference of two mixed numbers with like and unlike denominators
- model addition and subtraction of a given positive fraction or given mixed number
- solve a given problem involving the addition or subtraction of positive fractions or mixed numbers and determine if the solution is reasonable

PREREQUISITE SKILLS AND KNOWLEDGE

Prior to starting this unit, you should be able to…

- recognize improper fractions and mixed numbers
- change improper fractions to proper fractions and vice versa

Lesson 1   ADDING AND SUBTRACTING FRACTIONS WITH LIKE AND UNLIKE DENOMINATORS

ADDING FRACTIONS WITH LIKE DENOMINATORS PICTORALLY

Fractions compare parts of an object to the whole. The numerator represents the number of parts while the denominator represents the whole. For example, a pizza is cut into 8 slices. John eats 2 pieces and his sister eats 3 pieces of the pizza. The fraction representing the pieces of pizza John ate is $\frac{2}{8}$. The fraction representing the pieces of pizza John's sister ate is $\frac{3}{8}$. Together, they ate $\frac{5}{8}$ of the pizza.

Because the fractions have the same denominator, the numerators can be added. You can also show this operation using diagrams.

To add fractions with like denominators using diagrams, follow these steps:

Step 1
Draw a grid based on the factors of the denominator.

Step 2
Colour the parts of the grid that are equivalent to each numerator.

Step 3
Add the total number of coloured parts.

Example

Draw a diagram to solve $\frac{4}{9} + \frac{2}{9}$.

Solution
Step 1
Draw a grid based on the factors of the denominator.
The factors of the denominator are 1, 3, and 9. Use 3×3.

Step 2
Colour the parts of the grid that are equivalent to each numerator.
The numerators are 4 and 2. Use a different colour for each numerator.

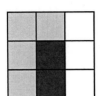

Step 3
Count the total number of coloured parts.
You have 6 coloured squares in total.

$$\frac{4}{9} + \frac{2}{9} = \frac{6}{9}$$

Notice that 2 of the 3 columns are shaded. The fraction $\frac{6}{9}$ can be

reduced to $\frac{2}{3}$.

$$\frac{4}{9} + \frac{2}{9} = \frac{2}{3}$$

ADDING FRACTIONS WITH LIKE DENOMINATORS NUMERICALLY

To add fractions with like denominators numerically, follow these steps:

Step 1
Add the numerators of the fractions while keeping the denominators
the same.

Step 2
Reduce the resulting fraction to lowest terms by dividing
the numerator and denominator by the greatest common factor (GCF)
if required.

Example

Add $\frac{4}{9}$ and $\frac{2}{9}$.

Solution

Step 1
Add the numerators of the fractions while keeping the denominators
the same.

$$\frac{4}{9} + \frac{2}{9} = \frac{4+2}{9}$$
$$= \frac{6}{9}$$

Step 2
Reduce the resulting fraction to lowest terms by dividing the numerator and denominator by the GCF.
The GCF is 3.

$$\frac{6 \div 3}{9 \div 3} = \frac{2}{3}$$

The sum of $\frac{4}{9} + \frac{2}{9} = \frac{2}{3}$.

Fractions with like denominators can also be subtracted. For example, a pizza is cut into 8 slices. John eats 2 pieces and his sister eats 3 pieces.

The fraction representing the pieces of pizza John ate is $\frac{2}{8}$.

The fraction representing the pieces of pizza John's sister ate is $\frac{3}{8}$.

Together, they ate $\frac{5}{8}$ of the pizza so only $\frac{3}{8}$ of the pizza is left.

Because the fractions have the same denominator, the numerators can be subtracted. You can also show this operation using diagrams. To subtract fractions with like denominators using diagrams, follow these steps:

Step 1
Draw a grid based on the factors of the denominator.

Step 2
Shade in the parts of the grid that are equivalent to the first numerator.

Step 3
Cross out the shaded parts equivalent to the second numerator.

Step 4
Count the total number of remaining shaded parts.

Example

Draw a diagram to solve $\frac{4}{9} - \frac{1}{9}$.

Solution

Step 1
Draw a grid based on the factors of the denominator. The factors of the denominator are 1, 3, and 9. Use 3 × 3.

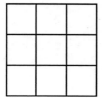

Step 2
Shade in the parts of the grid that are equivalent to the first numerator.
The first numerator is 4.

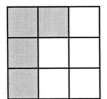

Step 3
Cross out the shaded parts equivalent to the second numerator.
The second numerator is 1.

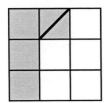

Step 4
Count the total number of remaining shaded parts.
There are 3 shaded squares left.

$$\frac{4}{9} - \frac{1}{9} = \frac{3}{9}$$

Notice that 1 column is left shaded. The fraction $\frac{3}{9}$ can be reduced to $\frac{1}{3}$.

The difference of $\frac{4}{9} - \frac{1}{9} = \frac{1}{3}$.

SUBTRACTING FRACTIONS WITH LIKE DENOMINATORS NUMERICALLY

To subtract fractions with like denominators numerically, follow these steps:

Step 1
Subtract the numerators of the fractions while keeping the denominators the same.

Step 2
Reduce the resulting fraction to lowest terms by dividing the numerator and denominator by the GCF if required.

ADDING FRACTIONS WITH UNLIKE DENOMINATORS

To add fractions with unlike denominators, follow these steps:

Step 1
Rewrite the fractions using the lowest common denominator (LCD).

Step 2
Add the numerators of the fractions while keeping the denominators the same.

Step 3
Reduce the resulting fraction to lowest terms by dividing the numerator and denominator by the GCF if required.

Example

Add $\dfrac{1}{4}$ and $\dfrac{2}{3}$.

Solution

Step 1
Rewrite the fractions using the LCD.

Write the multiples of each denominator until a common one appears.
Multiples of 3: 3, 6, 9, **12**, 15…
Multiples of 4: 4, 8, **12**, 16, 20…
The lowest common denominator of 3 and 4 is 12.

Multiply the numerator and the denominator of each fraction by the same factor.

$$\frac{1 \times 3}{4 \times 3} = \frac{3}{12} \qquad \frac{2 \times 4}{3 \times 4} = \frac{8}{12}$$

Step 2
Add the numerators of the fractions while keeping the denominators the same.

$$\frac{3}{12} + \frac{8}{12} = \frac{3 + 8}{12}$$
$$= \frac{11}{12}$$

Step 3
Reduce the resulting fraction to lowest terms.

The fraction is in lowest terms.

$$\frac{1}{4} + \frac{2}{3} = \frac{11}{12}$$

SUBTRACTING FRACTIONS WITH UNLIKE DENOMINATORS

To subtract fractions with unlike denominators, follow these steps:

Step 1
Rewrite the fractions using the LCD.

Step 2
Subtract the numerators of the fractions while keeping the denominators the same.

Step 3
Reduce the resulting fraction to lowest terms by dividing the numerator and denominator by the GCF if required.

Example

Subtract $\frac{1}{4}$ from $\frac{2}{3}$.

Solution

Step 1
Rewrite the fractions using the LCD.

Write the multiples of each denominator until a common one appears.
Multiples of 3: 3, 6, 9, **12**, 15…
Multiples of 4: 4, 8, **12**, 16, 20…
The lowest common denominator of 3 and 4 is 12.

Multiply the numerator and the denominator of each fraction by the same factor.

$$\frac{2 \times 4}{3 \times 4} = \frac{8}{12} \qquad \frac{1 \times 3}{4 \times 3} = \frac{3}{12}$$

Step 2
Subtract the numerators of the fractions while keeping the denominators the same.

$$\frac{8}{12} - \frac{3}{12} = \frac{8-3}{12} = \frac{5}{12}$$

Step 3
Reduce the resulting fraction to lowest terms.

The fraction is in lowest terms.

$$\frac{2}{3} - \frac{1}{4} = \frac{5}{12}$$

Lesson 2 MIXED NUMBERS

A **mixed number** is made up of two parts: a whole number and a fraction.

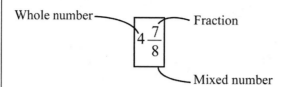

For example, Albert picked up 5 pizzas. Each pizza was cut into 8 slices. On the way home, he ate one piece. The amount of pizza remaining is 4 whole pizzas and $\frac{7}{8}$ of the fifth pizza. The mixed number $4\frac{7}{8}$ represents the amount of pizza left.

ADDING MIXED NUMBERS WITH LIKE DENOMINATORS

You can use one of two methods to add mixed numbers with the same denominators.

Method 1

Step 1

Change the mixed numbers to improper fractions using the following formula: $a\frac{b}{c} \rightarrow \frac{a \times c + b}{c}$

Step 2

Add the numerators of the fractions while keeping the denominators the same.

Step 3

Reduce the resulting improper fraction to lowest terms if required.

Step 4

Change the improper fraction to a mixed number using the following formula:

$$\text{numerator} \div \text{denominator} = \text{quotient} + \frac{\text{remainder}}{\text{denominator}}$$

Example

Calculate $2\frac{1}{6} + 3\frac{3}{6}$.

Solution

Step 1

Change the mixed numbers to improper fractions.

$$2\frac{1}{6} = \frac{2 \times 6 + 1}{6}$$
$$= \frac{13}{6}$$

$$3\frac{3}{6} = \frac{3 \times 6 + 3}{6}$$
$$= \frac{21}{6}$$

84

Step 2

Add the numerators of the fractions while keeping the denominators the same.

$$\frac{13}{6} + \frac{21}{6} = \frac{13 + 21}{6}$$
$$= \frac{34}{6}$$

Step 3

Reduce the resulting improper fraction to lowest terms.

Divide the numerator and denominator by the GCF (2).

$$\frac{34 \div 2}{6 \div 2} = \frac{17}{3}$$

Step 4

Change the improper fraction to a mixed number.
$17 \div 3 = 5 \text{ R2}$

$$\frac{17}{3} = 5\frac{2}{3}$$

$$2\frac{1}{6} + 3\frac{3}{6} = 5\frac{2}{3}$$

Method 2

Step 1

Add the whole numbers together.

Step 2

Add the fractions.

Step 3

Combine the whole number and fraction.

Step 4

Reduce the mixed number to lowest terms.

Example

Calculate $2\frac{1}{6} + 4\frac{3}{6}$.

Solution

Step 1

Add the whole numbers.
$2 + 4 = 6$

NOTES

Step 2
Add the fractions.

$$\frac{1}{6} + \frac{3}{6} = \frac{4}{6}$$

Step 3
Combine the whole numbers and fractions.

$$6 + \frac{4}{6} = 6\frac{4}{6}$$

Reduce the mixed number to lowest terms.

$$6\frac{4}{6} = 6\frac{4 \div 2}{6 \div 2}$$
$$= 6\frac{2}{3}$$

$$2\frac{1}{6} + 4\frac{3}{6} = 6\frac{2}{3}$$

ADDING MIXED NUMBERS WITH UNLIKE DENOMINATORS
Method 1
To add mixed numbers with unlike denominators, follow these steps:
Step 1
Change the mixed numbers to improper fractions.

Step 2
Rewrite the fractions with the LCD.

Step 3
Add the numerators of the equivalent fractions while keeping the denominators the same.

Step 4
Reduce the resulting fraction to lowest terms if required.

Step 5
Change the improper fraction to a mixed number using the following formula:

$$\text{numerator} \div \text{demoninator} = \text{quotient} + \frac{\text{remainder}}{\text{denominator}}$$

Example

Calculate $2\frac{1}{4}+1\frac{2}{3}$.

Solution

Step 1

Change the mixed numbers to improper fractions.

$$2\frac{1}{4}=\frac{2\times4+1}{4} \qquad\qquad 1\frac{2}{3}=\frac{1\times3+2}{3}$$

$$=\frac{9}{4} \qquad\qquad\qquad\qquad =\frac{5}{3}$$

Step 2

Rewrite the fractions with the LCD.

Write the multiples of each denominator until a common one appears.
Multiples of 3: 3, 6, 9, **12**, 15…
Multiples of 4: 4, 8, **12**, 16, and 20…
The lowest common denominator of 3 and 4 is 12.

Multiply the numerator and the denominator of each fraction by the same factor.

$$\frac{9\times3}{4\times3}=\frac{27}{12} \qquad\qquad \frac{5\times4}{3\times4}=\frac{20}{12}$$

Step 3

Add the numerators of the fractions while keeping the denominators the same.

$$\frac{27}{12}+\frac{20}{12}=\frac{27+20}{12}$$

$$=\frac{47}{12}$$

Step 4

Change the improper fraction to a mixed number.
$47\div12=3$ remainder 11

$$\frac{47}{12}=3\frac{11}{12}$$

The sum of $2\frac{1}{4}+1\frac{2}{3}=3\frac{11}{12}$.

SUBTRACTING MIXED NUMBERS WITH LIKE DENOMINATORS

Use one of two methods to subtract mixed numbers with the same denominators.

Method 1

Step 1

Change the mixed numbers to improper fractions using the following formula:

$$a\frac{b}{c} \rightarrow \frac{a \times c + b}{c}$$

Step 2

Subtract the numerators of the fractions while keeping the denominators the same.

Step 3

Reduce the resulting improper fraction to lowest terms if required.

Step 4

Change the improper fraction to a mixed number using the following formula:

$$\text{numerator} \div \text{demoninator} = \text{quotient} + \frac{\text{remainder}}{\text{denominator}}$$

Example

Calculate $3\frac{3}{6} - 2\frac{1}{6}$.

Solution

Step 1

Change the mixed number to an improper fraction.

$$3\frac{3}{6} = \frac{3 \times 6 + 3}{6} \qquad\qquad 2\frac{1}{6} = \frac{2 \times 6 + 1}{6}$$

$$= \frac{21}{6} \qquad\qquad\qquad = \frac{13}{6}$$

Step 2

Subtract the numerators of the fractions while keeping the denominators the same.

$$\frac{21}{6} - \frac{13}{6} = \frac{21 - 13}{6}$$

$$= \frac{8}{6}$$

Step 3
Reduce the resulting improper fraction to lowest terms.

The GCF of 8 and 6 is 2. Divide both the numerator and denominator by 2.

$$\frac{8 \div 2}{6 \div 2} = \frac{4}{3}$$

Step 4
Change the reduced improper fraction to a mixed number.
$$4 \div 3 = 1 \text{ R1}$$
$$\frac{4}{3} = 1\frac{1}{3}$$

$$3\frac{3}{6} - 2\frac{1}{6} = 1\frac{1}{3}$$

Method 2

Step 1
Subtract the whole numbers.

Step 2
Subtract the fractions.

Step 3
Combine the whole numbers and fractions and reduce the mixed number to lowest terms.

Example

Calculate $2\frac{4}{6} - 1\frac{2}{6}$.

Solution

Step 1
Subtract the whole numbers.
$$2 - 1 = 1$$

Step 2
Subtract the numerators of the fractions while keeping the denominators the same.
$$\frac{4}{6} - \frac{2}{6} = \frac{4-2}{6}$$
$$= \frac{2}{6}$$

Step 3

Add the whole number and the fraction.

$$1 + \frac{2}{6} = 1\frac{2}{6}$$

Reduce the fraction into lowest terms.

$$1\frac{2}{6} = 1\frac{2 \div 2}{6 \div 2}$$
$$= 1\frac{1}{3}$$
$$2\frac{4}{6} - 1\frac{2}{6} = 1\frac{1}{3}.$$

SUBTRACTING MIXED NUMBERS WITH UNLIKE DENOMINATORS

To subtract mixed numbers with unlike denominators, follow these steps:

Step 1

Change the mixed numbers to improper fractions using the following formula:

$$a\frac{b}{c} \rightarrow \frac{a \times c + b}{c}$$

Step 2

Rewrite the fractions using the LCD.

Step 3

Subtract the numerators of the equivalent fractions while keeping the denominators the same.

Step 4

Reduce the resulting improper fraction to lowest terms if required.

Step 5

Change the improper fraction to a mixed number using the following formula:

$$\text{numerator} \div \text{denominator} = \text{quotient} + \frac{\text{remainder}}{\text{denominator}}$$

Example

Calculate $2\dfrac{3}{4} - 1\dfrac{1}{3}$.

Solution

Step 1

Change the mixed numbers to improper fractions.

$$2\dfrac{3}{4} = \dfrac{2 \times 4 + 3}{4} \qquad\qquad 1\dfrac{1}{3} = \dfrac{1 \times 3 + 1}{3}$$

$$= \dfrac{11}{4} \qquad\qquad\qquad = \dfrac{4}{3}$$

Step 2

Rewrite the fractions using the LCD.

Write the multiples of each denominator until a common one appears.
Multiples of 3: 3, 6, 9, **12**, 15...
Multiples of 4: 4, 8, **12**, 16, 20…
The lowest common denominator of 3 and 4 is 12.

Multiply the numerator and the denominator of each fraction by the same factor.

$$\dfrac{11 \times 3}{4 \times 3} = \dfrac{33}{12} \qquad\qquad \dfrac{4 \times 4}{3 \times 4} = \dfrac{16}{12}$$

Step 3

Subtract the numerators of the fractions while keeping the denominators the same.

$$\dfrac{33}{12} - \dfrac{16}{12} = \dfrac{33 - 16}{12}$$

$$= \dfrac{17}{12}$$

Step 4

Change the reduced improper fraction to a mixed number.
$17 \div 12 = 1$ remainder 5

$$\dfrac{17}{12} = 1\dfrac{5}{12}$$

$$2\dfrac{3}{4} - 1\dfrac{1}{3} = 1\dfrac{5}{12}$$

Lesson 3 *PROBLEM SOLVING WITH FRACTIONS*

NOTES

You have to follow an order of operations when solving problems involving more than one operation to get the correct answer. Use the acronym **BEDMAS** to help remember the order of operations.

- **B**rackets—complete all operations inside a set of brackets. When brackets occur inside of brackets perform the operations inside the innermost brackets first and work your way outward.
- **E**xponents—evaluate the terms with exponents.
- **D**ivision/**M**ultiplication—complete the operations of division and multiplication in the order they appear from left to right.
- **A**ddition/**S**ubtraction—complete the operations of addition and subtraction in the order they appear from left to right.

The rules for working with the positive and negative signs still apply.

To solve word problems involving fractions, carefully read the question. Translate the words into a mathematical expression. Look for keywords indicating what operation to use to solve the problem. If necessary, underline or highlight the key words.

KEY WORDS
Add

- sum
- total
- altogether
- more than

Subtract

- difference
- less than
- take away
- taken from
- have left

SOLVING A PROBLEM INVOLVING FRACTIONS
To solve problems involving fractions, follow these steps:
Step 1
Identify the fractions and operational keywords.

Step 2
Write an expression to represent the problem.

Step 3
Solve the expression and reduce the answer to lowest terms if required.

Example

In total, James owns $2\frac{3}{5}$ acres of land, and his brother Art owns $3\frac{1}{5}$ acres.

One day, Sheila offers to buy $1\frac{2}{5}$ acres of the brothers' combined land.

If the brothers decide to sell the land to Sheila, how much land will they still own?

Solution

Step 1

Identify the fractions and the operational keywords.

James owns $2\frac{3}{5}$ acres of land. Art owns $3\frac{1}{5}$ acres of land.

Sheila wants to buy $1\frac{2}{5}$ acres of land.

"In total" means addition.
"How much land will they still own?" means subtraction.

Step 2

Write an expression to represent the problem.

$$\left(2\frac{3}{5}+3\frac{1}{5}\right)-1\frac{2}{5}$$

Step 3

Solve the expression and reduce the answer to lowest terms if required.

Change the mixed numbers into improper fractions.

$$2\frac{3}{5}=\frac{2\times5+3}{5} \qquad 3\frac{1}{5}=\frac{3\times5+1}{5} \qquad 1\frac{2}{5}=\frac{1\times5+2}{5}$$
$$=\frac{13}{5} \qquad\qquad =\frac{16}{5} \qquad\qquad =\frac{7}{5}$$

Follow the order of operations.

$$\left(\frac{13}{5}+\frac{16}{5}\right)-\frac{7}{5}$$

Brackets first.

$$\left(\frac{13}{5}+\frac{16}{5}\right)-\frac{7}{5}=\left(\frac{13+16}{5}\right)-\frac{7}{5}$$
$$=\frac{29}{5}-\frac{7}{5}$$

Complete the subtraction.

$$\frac{29}{5}-\frac{7}{5}=\frac{29-7}{5}$$
$$=\frac{22}{5}$$

93

Step 4

Change the improper fraction to a mixed number.

$22 \div 5 = 4$ R2

$$\frac{22}{5} = 4\frac{2}{5}$$

The brothers will still own $4\frac{2}{5}$ acres of land if they decide to sell some of it to Sheila.

Example

Everyone should drink $8\frac{1}{4}$ cups of water and $2\frac{2}{5}$ cups of milk a day. In total, how much fluid should everyone drink on a daily basis?

Solution

Step 1

Identify the fractions and the operational keywords.

$8\frac{1}{4}$ cups of water

$2\frac{2}{5}$ cups of milk

"In total" means addition.

Step 2

Write an expression to represent the problem.

$$8\frac{1}{4} + 2\frac{2}{5}$$

Step 3

Solve the expression and reduce the answer to lowest terms if required.

Change the mixed numbers into improper fractions.

$$8\frac{1}{4} = \frac{8 \times 4 + 1}{4} \qquad 2\frac{2}{5} = \frac{2 \times 5 + 2}{5}$$
$$\quad = \frac{33}{4} \qquad\qquad\quad = \frac{12}{5}$$

Rewrite the improper fractions with a common denominator.

The lowest common denominator of 4 and 5 is 20.

$$\frac{33 \times 5}{4 \times 5} = \frac{165}{20} \qquad \frac{12 \times 4}{5 \times 4} = \frac{48}{20}$$

Add the numerators while keeping the denominator the same.

$$\frac{165}{20} + \frac{48}{20} = \frac{165 + 48}{20}$$

$$= \frac{213}{20}$$

Step 4
Change the improper fraction to a mixed number.

$$213 \div 20 = 10 \text{ R}13$$

$$\frac{213}{20} = 10\frac{13}{20}$$

Everyone should drink $10\frac{13}{20}$ cups of fluid a day.

REVIEW SUMMARY

- Fractions are used to show the parts of a set or a whole.
- To add and subtract fractions pictorially draw the grid based on the factors of the denominator.
- To add or subtract fractions with like denominators, add or subtract the numerators of the fractions while keeping the denominators the same.
- To add or subtract fractions with unlike denominators, first identify the lowest common denominator (LCD), rewrite the fractions using the LCD, and add or subtract the numerators while keeping the denominators the same.
- Always reduce a fraction to lowest terms by dividing both the numerator and denominator by the greatest common factor (GCF).
- Improper fractions have a larger numerator than the denominator.
- Mixed numbers consist of a whole number and a fraction.
- When adding or subtracting mixed numbers, convert them into improper fractions before performing any operations on them.

THE CARTESIAN PLANE

When you are finished this unit, you will be able to…
- label the axes of a four quadrant Cartesian plane, and identify the origin
- identify the location of a given point in any quadrant of a Cartesian plane using an integral ordered pair
- identify the coordinates of the vertices of a given two-dimensional (2-D) shape on a Cartesian plane
- plot the point corresponding to a given integral ordered pair on a Cartesian plane with units of 1, 2, 5, or 10 on its axes
- draw shapes and designs on a Cartesian plane using given integral ordered pairs
- create shapes and designs and identify the points used to produce the shapes and designs in any quadrant of a Cartesian plane
- describe the horizontal and vertical movement required to move from a given point to another point on a Cartesian plane
- describe the positional change of the vertices of a given 2-D shape to the corresponding vertices of its image as a result of a transformation or successive transformations
- determine the distance between points along horizontal and vertical lines on a Cartesian plane
- perform a transformation or consecutive transformations on a given 2-D shape, and identify the coordinates of the vertices of the image
- describe the image resulting from the transformation of a given 2-D shape on a Cartesian plane by identifying the coordinates of the vertices of the image

PREREQUISITE SKILLS AND KNOWLEDGE

Prior to starting this unit, you should be able to…
- understand the concept of ordered pairs in the first quadrant of the coordinate plane
- create, analyze, and describe translations and reflections

Lesson 1 THE CARTESIAN PLANE

The Cartesian plane consists of two perpendicular number lines intersecting at point (0, 0). This point is called the origin.
The horizontal number line is the *x*-axis, and the vertical number line is the *y*-axis. These number lines divide the plane into four equal quadrants. Each quadrant has a set of ordered pairs that are unique to it. The quadrants are shown in the following diagram.

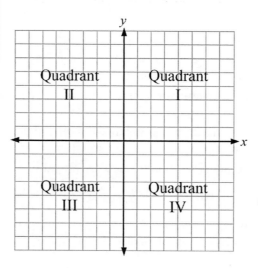

IDENTIFYING POINTS

A point on the Cartesian plane is defined using an ordered pair (*x*, *y*).
The first number in the ordered pair is called the *x*-coordinate. It tells you how far and in which direction to travel from the origin along the *x*-axis.

The second number in the ordered pair is called the *y*-coordinate.
It tells you how far and in which direction to travel from the origin along the *y*-axis.

To identify points on the Cartesian Plane, follow these steps:
Step 1
Determine the *x*-coordinate.

Step 2
Determine the *y*-coordinate.

Step 3
Write the ordered pair in the form (*x*, *y*).

Example

Identify the ordered pairs for points *A, B, C,* and *D.*

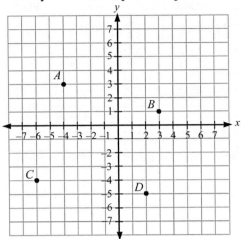

Solution

Step 1
Determine the *x*-coordinate for each point.
Count horizontally from the origin. If the point is to the right of the origin, it is a positive count; if it is to the left of the origin, it is a negative count.

Point *A* is 4 spaces to the left of the origin; its *x*-coordinate is –4.
Point *B* is 3 spaces to the right of the origin; its *x*-coordinate is 3.
Point *C* is 6 spaces to the left of the origin; its *x*-coordinate is –6.
Point *D* is 2 spaces to the right of the origin; its *x*-coordinate is 2.

Step 2
Determine the *y*-coordinate for each point.
Count vertically from the origin. If the point is above the origin, it is a positive count; if it is below the origin, it is a negative count.

Point *A* is 3 spaces above the origin; its *y*-coordinate is 3.
Point *B* is 1 space above the origin; its *y*-coordinate is 1.
Point *C* is 4 spaces below the origin; its *y*-coordinate is –4.
Point *D* is 5 spaces below the origin; its *y*-coordinate is –5.

Step 3
Write the ordered pair for each point.
Record the numbers in brackets, and separate them by a comma.
The *x*-coordinate goes first, and the *y*-coordinate goes second.

Point *A* has the ordered pair (–4, 3).
Point *B* has the ordered pair (3, 1).
Point *C* has the ordered pair (–6, –4).
Point *D* has the ordered pair (2, –5).

The following table will help you remember where the points on the Cartesian plane are located.

Quadrant	(Sign of x-coordinate, Sign of y-coordinate)
I	(pos, pos)
II	(neg, pos)
III	(neg, neg)
IV	(pos, neg)

PLOTTING POINTS AND MAKING SHAPES

When you plot points on the Cartesian plane, determine the placement of the x-coordinate first. Then, determine the placement of the y-coordinate. Finally, plot the point, and label it with a letter.

Example

Plot points $A(-2, 1)$, $B(0, 3)$, $C(2, 1)$, and $D(0, -3)$ on the Cartesian plane, and connect the points. Identify the shape created.

Solution

Step 1

Determine the placement of the x-coordinate for each point. If the coordinate is positive, move to the right of the origin. If the coordinate is negative, move to the left of the origin.
For point A, move 2 spaces to the left of the origin (-2).
For point B, do not move from the origin (0).
For point C, move 2 spaces to the right of the origin (2).
For point D, do not move from the origin (0).

Step 2

Determine the placement of the y-coordinate for each point.
Count vertically from the x-axis. If the coordinate is positive, move up from the x-axis. If the coordinate is negative, move down from the x-axis.
For point A, move 1 space up from the x-axis (1).
For point B, move 3 spaces up from the x-axis (3).
For point C, move 1 space up from the x-axis (1).
For point D, move 3 spaces down from the x-axis (-3).

Step 3
Plot the points. Place a dot at the intersection of the two lines, and label the point with the letter.

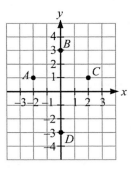

Step 4
Connect the points and identify the shape.

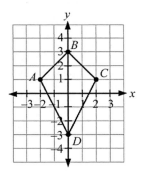

When the points are connected, the resulting shape is called a kite.

Lesson 2   TRANSFORMATIONS

Transformations are movements of points or figures from their original position to another position in the Cartesian Plane. The figure in the second position is called an **image**.

TRANSLATIONS

A **translation** occurs when a figure slides from its original position to a new position.

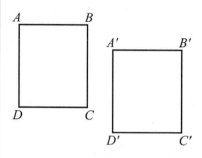

Congruent figures have the same shape and size, with all corresponding angles and all corresponding side lengths being equal.

The image is an exact, **congruent copy** of the original figure just placed in a new location. To show that a figure is an image, an apostrophe is placed on the letter that describes each vertex of the image.

In order to indicate the direction and distance of a translation, a translation arrow or an ordered pair is used.

A **translation arrow** indicates the direction and distance of a slide by indicating the starting (or original) position of the figure and the ending position of the image. A translation arrow is drawn from a vertex on the original figure to the corresponding vertex on the image.

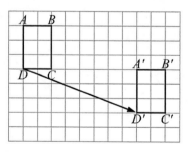

Example

Draw a translation arrow to represent a translation of 5 units right and 3 units up.

Solution

Pick a starting point. Draw an arrow that goes from the starting point to a position 5 units right and 3 units up.

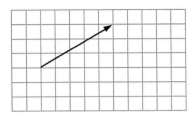

An **ordered pair** in the form [x, y] indicates the direction and distance of a translation.

The first number in an ordered pair represents horizontal movement along the *x*-axis on the Cartesian plane. A positive number represents movement to the right, and a negative number represents movement to the left.

The second number in the ordered pair represents vertical movement along the *y*-axis on the Cartesian plane. A positive number represents an upward movement, and a negative number represents a downward movement.

Example

Draw the translation [–3, 8] of figure *QRST*.

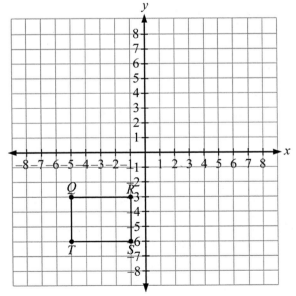

Solution

The translation is [–3, 8].

Since the *x*-coordinate is negative, the figure will move to the left 3 units. Then, since the *y*-coordinate is positive, the figure will move up 8 units to complete the translation [−3, 8].

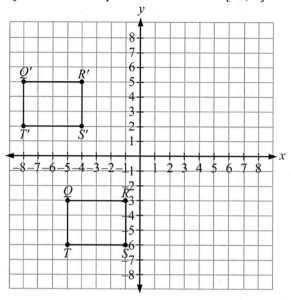

REFLECTIONS

A **reflection** occurs when a figure is flipped along a line of reflection or a mirror line to create a congruent image of the original figure, as illustrated below.

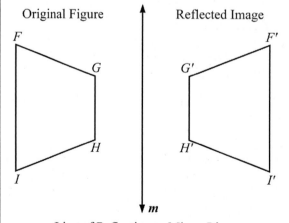

Line of Reflection or Mirror Line

Each vertex of a reflected image is the same distance from the line of reflection as the corresponding vertex of the original figure.

Example

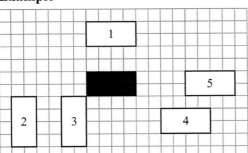

Which numbered figures are reflected images of the shaded figure?

Solution

Place mirror lines between the possible choices to determine which figures are reflections and which are not. There are three reflections in the given diagram, as illustrated.

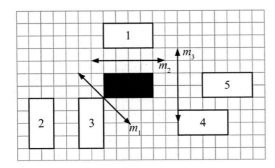

Figures 1, 3, and 5 are reflected images of the original shaded figure.

ROTATIONS

A **rotation** occurs when a figure is turned around a turn centre to create a congruent image of the original figure.

Rotations can be done in either a clockwise (cw) or counterclockwise (ccw) direction. Common rotation angles include 90° (a quarter turn), 180° (a half turn), and 270° (a three-quarter turn) in either a clockwise or counterclockwise direction.

A rotation is a turn.

A **turn centre** is the rotational point that a figure rotates around.

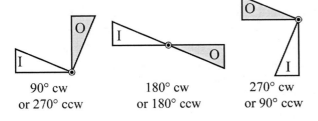

90° cw
or 270° ccw

180° cw
or 180° ccw

270° cw
or 90° ccw

NOTES

Example

Draw the rotated images of the shaded figure for rotations of

a) 90° cw to create image A   **b)** 90° ccw to create image B

c) 180° cw to create image C

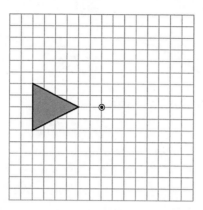

Solution

Trace the shaded figure, and mark the turn centre. Then, rotate the traced image 90° cw from the original shaded figure. Lift up the traced image, and draw the rotated image on the grid. Repeat this process for the other rotations of 90° ccw and 180° cw. Make sure to always start the rotations from the original figure.

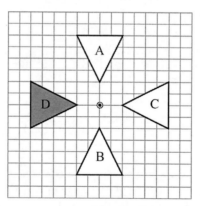

COMBINING TRANSFORMATIONS

When you are asked to make multiple transformations, always complete them in the order they are given in the question. Perform the first transformation using the original shape. Then, perform the second transformation using the transformed image. Continue to use the most recent image for any additional transformations.

Example

Quadrilateral *DEFG* has vertices *D*(2, –1), *E*(1, 2), *F*(4, 3), *G*(4, –1). Draw quadrilateral *DEFG* and its image after it is reflected about the *y*-axis and then translated 4 units right and 4 units up. Label final image *D"E"F"G"*.

Solution

Step 1

Draw the original shape on the Cartesian plane. Plot and label each point as given. Then, connect the points with line segments.

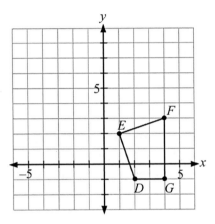

Step 2

Perform the first transformation using the original shape.
The first transformation is a reflection about the *y*-axis.
Plot and label each new point, then connect these points with line segments to form the reflected quadrilateral *D'E'F'G'*.

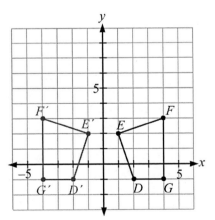

Step 3
Perform the second transformation using the transformed image.
The second transformation is a translation 4 units right and 4 units up.
Plot and label each new point, then connect these points with line
segments to form the translated quadrilateral $D''E''F''G''$.

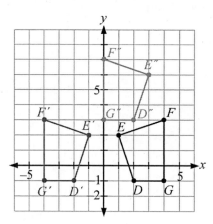

Example
Triangle ABC has the vertices $A(2, 2)$, $B(2, 6)$, $C(6, 2)$. The original
triangle is translated 1 unit to the right and 3 units down. Then it is
reflected about the y-axis. Determine the coordinates of triangle $A''B''C''$.

Solution
Step 1
Identify the coordinates of $A'B'C'$ after the first transformation
is applied.

The first transformation is a translation of 1 unit to the right and
3 units down. Add 1 to every x-coordinate, and subtract 3 from every
y-coordinate.
$A'(2+1, \ 2-3) = (3, \ -1)$
$B'(2+1, \ 6-3) = (3, \ 3)$
$C'(6+1, \ 2-3) = (7, \ -1)$

Step 2
Identify the coordinates of $A''B''C''$ after the second transformation
is applied.

The second transformation is a reflection about the
y-axis. The x-coordinates change to their opposite values while the
y-coordinates stay the same.
$A''(3, -1)$ becomes $(-3, -1)$
$B''(3, \ 3)$ becomes $(-3, \ 3)$
$C''(7, -1)$ becomes $(-7, -1)$

The coordinates of triangle $A''B''C''$ are $A''(-3, -1)$, $B''(-3, 3)$,
$C''(-7, 1)$.

REVIEW SUMMARY

- The Cartesian plane consists of two perpendicular number lines that intersect at point (0, 0) to create four equal quadrants.
- A point on the Cartesian plane is defined using an ordered pair (x, y). The first number in the ordered pair is the x-coordinate. It tells you how far and in which direction to travel from the origin along the x-axis. The second number in the ordered pair is the y-coordinate. It tells you how far and in which direction to travel from the origin along the y-axis.
  - To determine the x-coordinate, count along the x-axis. If the point is to the right of the origin, it is a positive count; if it is to the left of the origin, it is a negative count.
  - To determine the y-coordinate, count along the y-axis. If the point is above the origin, it is a positive count; if it is below the origin, it is a negative count.
- To plot points on the Cartesian plane, determine the placement of the x-coordinate first.
  Then, determine the placement of the y-coordinate. Finally, plot the point, and label it with a letter.
- The four quadrants contain coordinate pairs that have certain characteristics.
  - Quadrant I contains (pos, pos) coordinate pairs.
  - Quadrant II contains (neg, pos) coordinate pairs.
  - Quadrant III contains (neg, neg) coordinate pairs.
  - Quadrant IV contains (pos, neg) coordinate pairs.
- Transformations
  - A translation, which is the slide of a figure from one location to another, produces a congruent image. Translation directions can be given using an ordered pair or a translation arrow.
  - A reflection, which is a flip along a reflection line or mirror line, produces a congruent reflection image that is the mirror image of the original figure.
  - A rotation is a turn about a turn centre, which produces a congruent image. Turns are often done in 90°, 180°, or 270° movements in either a clockwise or counterclockwise direction.
- When you combine transformations, always complete them in the order they are given. Perform the first transformation on the original shape; then, perform the second transformation using the transformed image, and so on.

NOTES

PATTERNS

When you are finished this unit, you will be able to...

- formulate a linear relation to represent the relationship in a given pattern
- create a table of values for a given linear relation by substituting values for the variable
- create a table of values using a linear relation, and graph the table of values
- sketch the graph from a table of values created for a given linear relation, and describe the patterns found in the graph to draw conclusions
- describe using everyday language in spoken or written form the relationship shown on a graph to solve problems

PREREQUISITE SKILLS AND KNOWLEDGE

Prior to starting this unit, you should be able to...

- find approximate number values from a given graph
- create and extend patterns
- predict how patterns grow
- plot ordered pairs

Lesson 1 RELATING PATTERNS TO LINEAR RELATIONS

Determining a number pattern in mathematics involves looking closely at the information given in a problem for clues to help identify the pattern. Once a pattern is found, the pattern can be used to continue a sequence of numbers or predict a possible *n*th value.

Patterns can be represented by linear relations. A **relation** is anything that connects one set of information to another. A **linear relation** is a relationship between two variables that is represented as a straight line on a graph.

Example

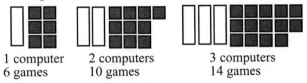

1 computer   2 computers   3 computers
6 games   10 games   14 games

These diagrams illustrate the relationship between the number of computers and computer games sold at an electronics store.

a) Using words, describe the relationship between the number of computers and computer games sold.

Solution

For every computer sold after the first computer, four more computer games are also sold.

b) Use the pattern to predict how many games would be sold if 12 computers were sold.

Solution

Make a table to help continue the pattern.

Number of Computers Sold	Number of Computer Games Sold
1	6
2	10
3	14
4	18
5	22
6	26
7	30
8	34
9	38
10	42
11	46
12	50

If 12 computers were sold then 50 computer games would also be sold.

NOTES

You can also determine the number of computer games sold by using a linear relation. The relationship between the number of computer games sold (g) and the number of computers sold (c) is represented by $g = 4c + 2$.

To calculate the number of computer games sold when 12 computers are sold, 12 is substituted for c and solve for g.

$$g = 4c + 2$$
$$= 4(12) + 2$$
$$= 48 + 2$$
$$= 50$$

There would be 50 computer games sold if 12 computers were sold.

It is possible to represent an everyday situation as a linear relation.

To write a context for a given linear relation, follow these steps:

Step 1
Determine what the first term could represent.

Step 2
Determine what the constant could mean.

Step 3
Create a context that fits within those terms.

Example
Give a possible context for the linear relation $20p + 50$.

Solution
Step 1
Determine what the first term could represent.
Assuming the variable is meaningful, p could represent person and 20 multiplies p.

Step 2
Determine what the constant could mean.
A constant 50 is added to $20p$. It could represent a booking fee.

Step 3
Create a context that fits within those terms.
The school is having a party. The caterer charges $20 a person plus a $50 booking fee.

The solution will vary depending on what the first term represents.

A linear relation can be used to get the same results as when using a table of values.

Lesson 2   TABLE OF VALUES AND GRAPHING

A **table of values** is a chart that shows the relationship between two variables, one is the input number and the other is the output number.

The numbers that are inputted into the relation first are called the input numbers. The values that result after the relation has been evaluated are called the output numbers.

A table of values is organized in such a way that the input number is listed in the first column and the output number is listed in the second column.

Input Number (x)	Output Number (y)

When given a linear relation, substitute in the given number and evaluate for the unknown variable.

Example

Create a table of values for the linear relation $y = 4x + 2$.

Solution

Step 1

Set up a table of values and use any numbers you like to represent x.

x	y
1	
2	
3	
4	

Step 2

Substitute in the values for x and evaluate the linear relation for y.

x	y
1	$4(1) + 2 = 6$
2	$4(2) + 2 = 10$
3	$4(3) + 2 = 14$
4	$4(4) + 2 = 18$

When graphing a linear relation, follow these steps:
Step 1
Create a table of values to determine the set of ordered pairs.

Step 2
Identify the ordered pairs.

Step 3
Plot the ordered pairs on a graph.

Example
Graph the relation represented in the given table of values.

Time (h)	Distance (km)
0	0
1	10
2	20
3	30

Solution
Step 1
Identify the ordered pairs.
The input and corresponding output number create the ordered pair in the form (x, y).

Time (h)	Distance (km)	Ordered Pair
0	0	(0, 0)
1	10	(1, 10)
2	20	(2, 20)
3	30	(3, 30)

There are no units of measurement placed in the ordered pairs.

Step 2
Label the x- and y- axis.
Plot the ordered pairs on the graph.

For each ordered pair, start at the origin and move horizontally to the value of the x-coordinate. Then, move vertically to the value of the y-coordinate. Give the graph a title.

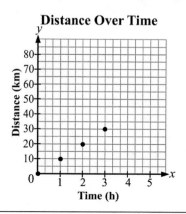

In a linear relation, the points will form a straight line.

To interpret a graph that represents a linear relation, observe the pattern formed by the points.
- If the points rise to the right, that means that as one value increases, so does the other value.
- If the points fall to the right, that means that as one value increases, the other value decreases.
- If the points have no distinct pattern, then there is no relationship between them.

Example

One day, Sandy decided to make a graph of the distance she walked in relation to the time it took to walk that distance. Then she plotted three points.

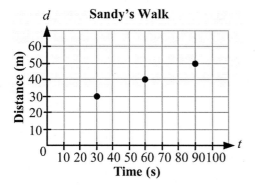

Determine the relationship between time and distance during Sally's walk.

Solution
Since the points are rising to the right, the pattern indicates that the more time Sally spends walking, the more distance she covers.

NOTES

REVIEW SUMMARY

- A linear relation can be created from a relationship found in a pattern. The linear relation can be used to make predictions of future events without drawing more diagrams or extending a table of values.
- When graphing a relation, a table of values is used to create a set of ordered pairs that are plotted on a graph as points or coordinates.
- To graph ordered pairs, start at the origin, move along the *x*-axis to find the value of the *x*-coordinate, and then move up vertically to the value of the *y*-coordinate.
- To interpret a graph that represents a linear relation, observe the pattern formed by the points.
  - If the points rise to the right, that means that as one value increases, so does the other value.
  - If the points fall to the right, that means that as one value increases, the other value decreases.
  - If the points have no distinct pattern, then there is no relationship between them.

EXPRESSIONS AND EQUATIONS

When you are finished this unit, you will be able to…
- evaluate algebraic expressions given the value of the variable
- explain the difference between an expression and an equation
- apply preservation of equality to solve equations
- demonstrate how to solve a one-step, single-variable, first-degree equation by using concrete materials or diagrams
- solve and verify one-step linear equations
- solve and verify two-step linear equations

PREREQUISITE SKILLS AND KNOWLEDGE

Prior to starting this unit, you should be able to…
- create expressions to describe patterns and relationships
- represent a given problem with an equation
- model the preservation of equality for addition, subtraction, multiplication, and division

Lesson 1 *EVALUATING EXPRESSIONS*

NOTES

Brackets
Exponents
Division
Multiplication
Addition
Subtraction

Multiply or divide in order from left to right.
Add or subtract in order from left to right

Mathematical **expressions** consist of numbers, variables (x, y, xy), and operational symbols ($+$, $-$). Expressions can be as short as a single term, or they can consist of two or more terms joined by an operation. **Variables** are letters used to represent numbers when the values are not known in an expression. If the value of a variable is given, it is possible to solve the expression by substituting in the given number. When evaluating expressions, the order of operations still applies. BEDMAS tells you in what order to perform the required operations.

For more complicated expressions, place the value of the variable in brackets. This makes it easier to recognize the order in which to perform the operations.

Example

What is the value of $5v - 5$ if $v = 3$?

Solution
Step 1
Substitute the value of the variable into the expression using brackets.
$5v - 5$
$= 5(3) - 5$

Step 2
Evaluate the expression using BEDMAS.
$5(3) - 5$
$= 15 - 5$
$= 10$

If brackets are not used, a common mistake is to write 53 instead of 5(3) in the second line of the calculation. This will result in an incorrect answer.

Equations and expressions are similar in that they both can contain constant terms, numerical coefficients, and variables.

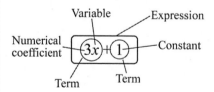

But they have one main difference: equations have an equal sign and can be solved, whereas expressions do not have an equal sign and can have an infinite number of answers depending on the values used for the variable.

Example

Given the following mathematical statements, identify which one is an expression and which one is an equation: $v - 4$ and $v - 4 = 8$.

Solution
The expression is $v - 4$ because it is not set equal to any particular value. The equation is $v - 4 = 8$ because it is equal to 8.

Lesson 2   PRESERVING EQUALITY

Preserving equality means to retain the same value on both sides of the equation while performing any mathematical operation.

Let's use algebra tiles to model the preservation of equality.

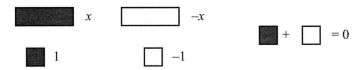

Algebra tiles can be used to model the preservation of equality. Different shape tiles are used to represent the variable and constant. The colour represents positive and negative values.

For example, $x + 4 = 10$ is modelled using the following arrangement of algebra tiles:

When 2 unit tiles are added to both sides of the equal sign, the arrangement of algebra tiles becomes:

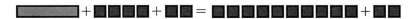

The equation becomes:
$$x + 4 + 2 = 10 + 2$$
$$x + 6 = 12$$

In the equations $x + 4 = 10$ and $x + 6 = 12$, x represents the same value. Therefore, equality has been preserved.

To preserve equality, the most important thing to remember is that an operation performed on the left side of the equal sign must also be made to the right side.

Example
Using each of the following operations addition, subtraction, multiplication, division, and the number 4, manipulate $2n = 8$ while preserving equality.

Solution
Addition:　　　$2n = 8$
　　　　　　$2n + 4 = 8 + 4$
　　　　　　$2n + 4 = 12$

Subtraction:　　$2n = 8$
　　　　　　$2n - 4 = 8 - 4$
　　　　　　$2n - 4 = 4$

Multiplication:　　$2n = 8$
　　　　　　$2n \times 4 = 8 \times 4$
　　　　　　　$8n = 32$

Division: $2n = 8$
$$2n \div 4 = 8 \div 4$$
$$\frac{n}{2} = 2$$

Substitute 4 for n to verify that equality was preserved in each of the equations.

Addition: $2n + 4 = 12$
$$2(4) + 4 = 12$$
$$8 + 4 = 12$$
$$12 = 12$$

Subtraction: $2n - 4 = 4$
$$2(4) - 4 = 4$$
$$8 - 4 = 4$$
$$4 = 4$$

Multiplication: $2n \times 4 = 32$
$$2(4) \times 4 = 32$$
$$8 \times 4 = 32$$
$$32 = 32$$

Division: $2n \div 4 = 2$
$$2(4) \div 4 = 2$$
$$8 \div 4 = 2$$
$$2 = 2$$

SOLVING EQUATIONS USING PRESERVATION OF EQUALITY

In order to preserve equality of an equation, it is important to perform the *same operation* to both sides of the equation.

Preserving equality is a fundamental principle that is used to identify the value of an unknown variable in an equation.

Algebra tiles can be used to determine the value of an unknown variable in an equation.

Example

Solve the equation $x + 5 = 10$ using algebra tiles and a balance scale.

Solution

Step 1

Draw a diagram using algebra tiles to represent the equation.

The equation $x + 5 = 10$ can be represented pictorially using the following arrangement of algebra tiles on a balance scale.

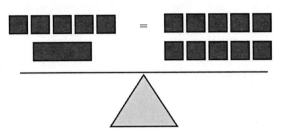

On the left side of the balance, there is 1 shaded x-tile and 5 shaded unit tiles. This represents $x + 5$.

On the right side of the balance, there are 10 shaded unit tiles. This represents 10.

Step 2

Perform the opposite operation to both sides of the equation.

The opposite of adding 5 is to subtract 5, so remove 5 squares from each side of the balance scale.

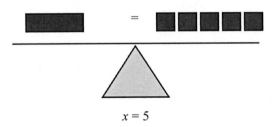

$$x = 5$$

When there is one x-tile left on either side of the balance, you have solved for the value of x.

In this case, $x = 5$.

It is good practice to check your answer by substituting the value of x back into the original equation.

$$x + 5 = 10$$
$$(5) + 5 = 10$$
$$10 = 10$$

Since both sides of the equation are equal, equality was preserved.

The main goal in one-step equation solving is to isolate the variable.

Removing five squares from each side does not unbalance the scale, so both sides of the balance scale are still equal to each other.

Checking an answer by substitution will verify if the calculated answer is correct or not. If the sides of the equation do not match, then the calculated answer is incorrect.

Lesson 3 SOLVING ONE-STEP AND TWO-STEP EQUATIONS

NOTES

One step linear equations require the use of one operation in order to solve for the variable.

Two step linear equations require the use of two operations in order to solve for the variable.

SOLVING ONE-STEP LINEAR EQUATIONS

One-step equations can be solved using the principles of preservation of equality.

Remember the operation that is performed on the left side of the equation must also be performed on the right side of the equation.

To verify your answer, substitute the value of the variable back into the original equation.

Example

Find the value of n in the equation $n + 6 = 10$.

Solution

Step 1

Perform the opposite operation to both sides of the equation.
The opposite of adding 6 is subtracting 6. Subtract 6 from both sides of the equation.

$$n + 6 = 10$$
$$n + 6 - 6 = 10 - 6$$
$$n = 4$$

Step 2

Check by substitution.

$$n + 6 = 10$$
$$(4) + 6 = 10$$
$$10 = 10$$

Example

Solve for n in the equation $3n = 45$.

Solution

Step 1

Perform the opposite operation to both sides of the equation.

The opposite of multiplying n by 3 is dividing n by 3.

$$3n = 45$$
$$\frac{\cancel{3}n}{\cancel{3}} = \frac{\cancel{45}^{15}}{\cancel{3}}$$
$$n = 15$$

Step 2
Check by substitution.

$$3n = 45$$
$$3(15) = 45$$
$$45 = 45$$

Example

Solve for t in the equation $\dfrac{t}{4} = 8$.

Solution

Step 1
Perform the opposite operation to both sides of the equation.
The opposite of dividing t by 4 is multiplying t by 4.

$$\frac{t}{4} = 8$$
$$\frac{(4)t}{4} = 8(4)$$
$$t = 32$$

Step 2
Check by substitution.

$$\frac{t}{4} = 8$$
$$\frac{(32)}{4} = 8$$
$$8 = 8$$

SOLVING TWO-STEP LINEAR EQUATIONS

When solving two-step equations, you use the same techniques used in solving one-step equations except you will perform two operations rather than just one.

Example

Solve for x in the equation $4x - 1 = 11$.

Solution

Step 1
Perform the opposite operation of the constant on both sides of the equation.

The opposite operation of subtracting 1 is adding 1. Add 1 to both sides.

$$4x - 1 = 11$$
$$4x - 1 + 1 = 11 + 1$$
$$4x = 12$$

Step 2

Perform the opposite operation of the variable on both sides of the equation.

The opposite of multiplying x by 4 is to divide by 4.
Divide both sides by 4.

$$\frac{4x}{4} = \frac{12}{4}$$
$$x = 3$$

Step 3

Check by substitution.

$$4x - 1 = 11$$
$$4(3) - 1 = 11$$
$$12 - 1 = 11$$
$$11 = 11$$

PROBLEM SOLVING WITH LINEAR EQUATIONS

Problem solving in mathematics can often be done algebraically using an equation to find an answer instead of guessing and checking to find the answer.

To solve problems using a linear equation, follow these steps:

Step 1

Define the variable.

Step 2

Write the equation to represent the situation.

Step 3

Isolate the variable by preserving equality on both sides of the equation.

Step 4

Check your answer by substituting the calculated value of the variable back into the original equation.

Example

Pearl has some photographs and divides them into sets of 4 per page to put into her photo album. Pearl makes exactly 25 sets of photographs. How many photographs does Pearl have in total?

Solution

Step 1

Define the variable.

Let p equal the total number of photographs in the album.

Step 2

Write the equation.

Since Pearl divides all the photographs into sets of four and makes exactly 25 sets of photographs, the equation that represents this situation is $\dfrac{p}{4} = 25$.

Step 3

Isolate the variable to find the value of p.

$$\frac{p}{4} = 25$$
$$4\left(\frac{p}{4}\right) = 4(25)$$
$$p = 100$$

Step 4

Check by substitution.

$$\frac{p}{4} = 25$$
$$\frac{(100)}{4} = 25$$
$$25 = 25$$

Pearl has 100 photographs in her photo album.

REVIEW SUMMARY

- A variable is a letter used to represent a number when its value is unknown. Different variables represent different numbers.
- An expression is a combination of at least one variable, number, and mathematical operation.
- Expressions, unlike equations, have an infinite number of answers because the variable can have any value.
- Expressions can be evaluated by substituting a given number for a variable into the expression and then using order of operations to find the answer.
- Equations differ from expressions because they include the equal sign, so there is only one number that the variable can represent.
- Equations can be solved using algebra tiles or algebraically by performing the opposite mathematical operation on both sides of the equation.
- It is good practice to check the answer by substituting the calculated value into the original equation to see if both sides of the equation are equal to each other.

126

GEOMETRIC CONSTRUCTIONS

When you are finished this unit, you will be able to…

- describe examples of parallel line segments, perpendicular line segments, perpendicular bisectors, and angle bisectors in the environment
- identify line segments on a given diagram that are parallel or perpendicular
- draw a line segment perpendicular to another line segment, and explain why they are perpendicular
- draw a line segment parallel to another line segment, and explain why they are parallel
- draw the bisector of a given angle using more than one method, and verify that the resulting angles are equal
- draw the perpendicular bisector of a line segment using more than one method, and verify the construction

PREREQUISITE SKILLS AND KNOWLEDGE

Prior to starting this unit, you should be able to…

- measure angles using a protractor
- draw angles
- know the definition of parallel and perpendicular lines
- use a compass

Lesson 1 LINE SEGMENTS

A **line** is actually an infinite number of points all arranged in a row. The arrows on either end of the line indicate that it continues on in either direction indefinitely.

A **line segment** consists of all the points between two given points on a line.

A
B

Perpendicular lines (⊥) are lines that intersect at exactly 90° to each other. For example, lampposts are perpendicular to the ground because they intersect the ground at 90°. Table legs are perpendicular to a table top because they intersect the table at 90°.

When drawing perpendicular lines, a square is placed in the corner of one of the angles to indicate that the lines are perpendicular.

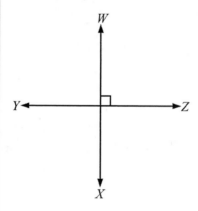

Line segment *WX* is perpendicular to line segment *YZ* because they intersect at 90° to each other.

Use the following example to learn how to draw perpendicular lines using a compass and a straight edge.

Example

Draw a perpendicular line segment from point *K*.

Solution

Step 1
Draw line segment.

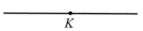

K

Label point K.

Step 2
Place the point of the compass on point K, and draw two small arcs (with the same spread) that cut the line segment.

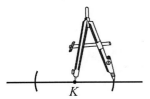

Step 3
Place the compass point on one arc with a spread of about three-quarters of the distance between the two arcs, and draw a semicircle.

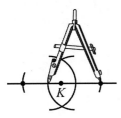

Repeat this procedure on the other side of the line.

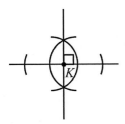

Step 4
Connect the two points of intersection.

Parallel lines are line segments that remain the same distance apart from one another, which means they never cross or intersect each other.
For example, railroad tracks are parallel lines because they remain an equal distance apart and they never intersect.

When drawing parallel lines, arrows are drawn along each of the lines to indicate the lines are parallel.

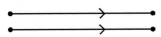

Use the following example to learn how to draw parallel lines using a compass and a straight edge.

NOTES

Example

Draw two parallel line segments 2 cm apart and 9 cm long.

Solution

Step 1

Draw a line segment.

Draw the first line segment 9 cm long. Label each of the points at the ends of the line with a letter.

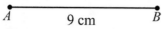

A   9 cm   *B*

Step 2

Draw a circle with a radius equal to the distance the two lines need to be apart.

Spread the two ends of the compass 2 cm apart. Place the point of the compass on one end of the line segment, and draw a circle. Repeat on the other end, keeping the same spread.

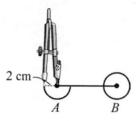

2 cm

A   *B*

Step 3

Use a straight edge to draw a line segment connecting the top of the two circles.

A   *B*

Lesson 2 PERPENDICULAR AND ANGLE BISECTORS

When a line segment is divided into two equal halves by another line, the segment has been **bisected**.

The line that was drawn is called the **bisector**. The bisected line segments are marked with the same number of ticks to indicate that they are equal in measure.

Bi means "two" and *sect* means "cut."

When the bisector divides the line segment in half at 90°, it is called a **perpendicular bisector**.

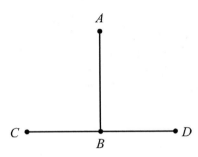

To draw a perpendicular bisector for a line segment using a compass and a straight edge, follow these steps:

Step 1
Draw the line segment.

Step 2
Draw the first arc.

Place the compass on one end or point of the line segment. Draw an arc or circle that crosses the line segment close to the other end.

Step 3
Draw the second arc.

Repeat the process from the other end of the line. Keep the same spread.

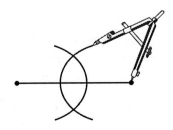

Step 4
Draw the perpendicular bisector.

Use a straight edge to draw a line segment connecting the two points where the arcs meet.

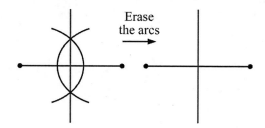

Erase
the arcs

The new line is a perpendicular bisector to the original line segment.

Use the steps in the following example to draw a perpendicular bisector using a right triangle.

Example

Line segment *EF* is 10 cm long. Draw the line segment and its perpendicular bisector using a right triangle.

Solution

Step 1
Draw line segment *EF* 10 cm long.

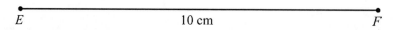

E   10 cm   *F*

Step 2
Divide the length by 2.
$10 \text{ cm} \div 2 = 5 \text{ cm}$

Step 3
Plot a point *D*, 5 cm from either side. Place the corner of the right triangle at point *D*. Draw a line segment, making sure to extend the line above and below line segment *EF*.

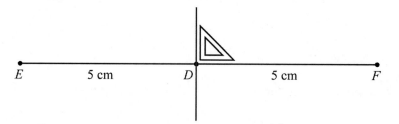

E   5 cm   *D*   5 cm   *F*

Just as a line segment can be bisected, an angle can also be bisected. When an angle is divided into two equal halves by a line, the angle has been **bisected**. The line that cuts an angle into two equal halves is called the **angle bisector**.

The angles are marked with the same symbol to indicate that they are equal in measure.

To draw an angle bisector using a protractor, follow these steps:

Step 1
Draw and label angle if it is not provided.

Step 2
Calculate the size of the bisected angle.

Step 3
Use the protractor to make this angle.

Step 4
Draw the angle bisector.

Connect the vertex of the original angle with the point making the bisected angle.

Example

Angle *ABC* is 100°. Draw ∠*ABC* and the angle bisector using a protractor.

Solution

Step 1
Draw and label the angle.

Draw line segment *AB*. Use a protractor to add line segment *BC* at 100°.

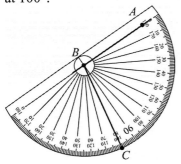

Step 2
Calculate the size of the bisected angle.

Divide the measure of the angle by 2. $100 \div 2 = 50$

NOTES

Step 3
Use a protractor to mark this angle.

Place the zero line on one of the line segments. Follow the outside numbers to 50. Plot point *U* at 50°.

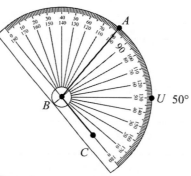

Step 4
Draw the angle bisector using the straight edge of the protractor. Use a straight edge to connect point *B* to point *U*.

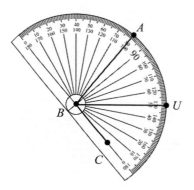

Another way to bisect the angle is with a compass and aruler, using the following steps:

Step 1
Draw and label the angle if it is not already provided.

Step 2
Draw an arc to intersect the two line segments of the angle.

Step 3
From both points of intersection between the arc and the arms of the angle, draw two more intersecting arcs.

Step 4
Using a ruler, draw a line from the angle to this intersection point.

134

Example

Angle *ABC* is 100°. Using a compass, draw ∠*ABC* and the angle bisector.

Solution

Step 1

Draw and label the angle.
Draw line segment AB. Use a protractor to add line segment BC at 100°.

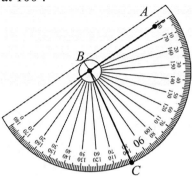

Step 2

Draw an arc to intersect the two line segments of the angle.
Place the point of the compass on point *B*. Draw an arc intersecting line segment *AB* and line segment *BC*. Label the points of intersection as *F* and *G*.

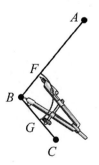

Step 3

Draw two more intersecting arcs from points *F* and *G*. Place the point of the compass on point *F*. Draw an arc toward the middle of the angle. Repeat the process at point *G*, keeping the size of the compass opening the same. Label the point of intersection as *U*.

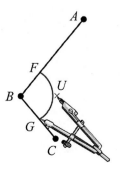

Step 4

Draw a line from the angle to the intersection point.
Use a straight edge to connect point *B* to point *U*.

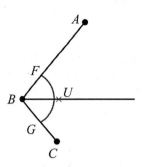

Step 5

Verify that the angles are equal. Use a protractor to measure the two new angles.

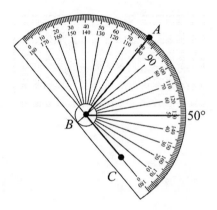

REVIEW SUMMARY

- Perpendicular lines are two lines that intersect at exactly 90°.
- Parallel lines are lines that are always the same distance apart from each other; that is, they do
  not intersect.
- An angle bisector divides an angle into two equal or congruent parts.
  A compass can be used to create arcs (or circles) to determine the exact location to divide an angle into congruent parts.
- An angle bisector can also be created using a protractor and a straight edge.
- A perpendicular bisector divides a line segment at the exact centre at a 90° angle. A compass can be used to create arcs (or circles) used to determine the exact location to divide a line segment in half.
- A perpendicular bisector can also be created using a right triangle and a straight edge.

CIRCLES

When you are finished this unit, you will be able to…
- illustrate and explain that the diameter is twice the radius in a given circle
- illustrate and explain that the circumference is approximately three times the diameter in a given circle
- explain, using an illustration, that the sum of the central angles of a circle is 360°
- draw a circle with a given radius or diameter, with and without a compass
- explain that for all circles, pi is the ratio of the circumference to the diameter and its value is approximately 3.14
- solve a given problem involving circles
- identify common attributes of circle graphs
- create and label a circle graph
- translate percentages displayed in a circle graph into quantities to solve a given problem.
- interpret a given circle graph to answer questions

PREREQUISITE SKILLS AND KNOWLEDGE

Prior to starting this unit, you should be able to…
- calculate and solve problems involving measurement
- demonstrate an understanding of circles
- estimate and measure angles using a protractor
- sketch and draw an angle when the size is given
- read and interpret graphs

Lesson 1 INTRODUCTION TO CIRCLES

Bicycle tires, inline skate wheels, and compact discs are just a few examples of circles. The distance around a circle is called its **circumference** (C).

The distance between a point along the edge of the circle to a point on the exact opposite side of the circle is called the **diameter** (d). The diameter goes through the centre of the circle, and it cuts the circle into two halves.

The **radius** (r) of a circle is the distance from the centre of a circle to a point along the edge of the circle; it is equal to half the value of the diameter.

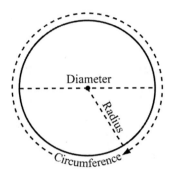

Using a given point for the centre of the circle and a radius or diameter, it is possible to construct a diagram of any circle. You will need a ruler and a compass. The ruler is used to measure out the radius, while the compass will draw the actual circle. The radius is used to determine the distance between the pencil tip and the pivot point of the compass.

To draw a circle, follow these steps:
Step 1
Determine the value of r.

Step 2
Draw the line segment using a ruler.

Step 3
Draw the circle using a compass.

Example
Draw a circle with a radius of 4 cm using a compass.

> *Solution*
> **Step 1**
> Determine the value of r.
> The radius is 4 cm.
>
> **Step 2**
> Draw a line segment 4 cm long using a ruler.

Step 3
Draw the circle using a compass.

Place the pointed end of the compass at one end of the line segment. Place a pencil at the other end of the line segment. Rotate the pencil tip around the pivot point until a circle is drawn.

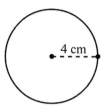

If a circle is cut into sectors, the sum of all the central angles always equals 360°. This is proven using two diameters.

When two diameters intersect at 90°, four equal right angles are formed. A right angle is equal to 90°.
$4 \times 90 = 360°$

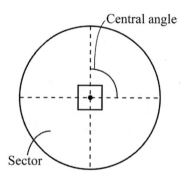

Knowing that all the central angles in a circle must add up to 360° allows you to calculate missing angle measures.

Example
The two unknown angles are equal.

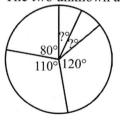

What is the angle measure of each sector?

Solution
Step 1
Calculate the total of the known angles.
$80 + 110 + 120 = 310$

Step 2
Calculate the unknown angle measure.

Subtract the total of the known angles from 360°.
$360° - 310° = 50°$

Because there are two equal angles, divide 50° in half.
$50° \div 2 = 25°$

The missing angles are 25° each.

CIRCUMFERENCE

The circumference of any circle divided by its diameter gives the mathematical constant pi (π). **Pi** is a non-repeating, non-terminating decimal number.

$$\pi = \frac{C}{d}$$
$$= 3.141\,592\,653\,589\ldots$$

In mathematics, the value of π is often shortened to 3.14.

The following formulas show the relationship between the circumference, diameter, and radius of a circle. They are also useful when solving for the missing dimension of a circle. If the diameter or radius of a circle is known, the circumference of a circle can be calculated using one of the formulas.

Dimensions of a Circle	Formula
Circumference (if diameter is known)	$C = \pi d$
Circumference (if radius is known)	$C = 2\pi r$
Diameter	$d = \dfrac{C}{\pi}$
Radius	$r = \dfrac{C}{2\pi}$

To calculate any of the dimensions, follow these steps:

Step 1
Choose the appropriate formula using the given values.

Step 2
Substitute in the known values.

Step 3
Solve for the unknown.

Example

Find the circumference of a circle if the diameter of the circle is 5 cm.

Solution

Step 1

Choose the appropriate formula.

Use the formula $C = \pi d$ to find the circumference (C).

Step 2

Substitute in the known values.

The diameter is 5 cm, and π is 3.14.

Step 3

Solve for the unknown.

$$
\begin{aligned}
C &= \pi d \\
&= 3.14 \times 5 \\
&= 15.7 \text{ cm}
\end{aligned}
$$

Therefore, the circumference of the circle is 15.7 cm.

Example

The circumference of a car tire is 120 cm. Find the diameter of the tire to the nearest tenth of a centimetre.

Solution

Step 1

Choose the appropriate formula using the given values.

Use the formula $d = \dfrac{C}{\pi}$ to find the diameter.

Step 2

Substitute in the known values.

The circumference is 120 cm and π is 3.14.

Step 3

Solve for the unknown.

$$
\begin{aligned}
d &= \frac{C}{\pi} \\
&= \frac{120}{3.14} \\
&= 38.216\,560\,51\ldots \text{ cm}
\end{aligned}
$$

Rounded to the nearest tenth, the diameter is 38.2 cm.

Lesson 2 CONSTRUCTING CIRCLE GRAPHS

Circle graphs represent data that constitutes parts of a whole. The data is divided into parts called sectors. The circle represents 100% while each sector represents a part of 100%. This allows you to easily compare each sector to one another. Each percentage corresponds to an equivalent number of degrees in the circle.

To construct a circle graph, follow these steps:

Step 1
If necessary, convert the data into decimal numbers.

Step 2
Calculate each percentage as an angle in degrees.

Step 3
Draw a circle. Then draw each of the angles using a protractor and straight edge.

Step 4
Label the sectors with a title and the corresponding percentage.

Example
The table shows Jolanda's movie rentals by category for the past three months.

Category	Number of Rentals
Drama	10
Comedy	7
Action	2
Horror	1

Construct a circle graph to represent this information.

Solution
Step 1
Convert the data into decimal numbers.

Divide each part of the data by the total data.
The total number of movie rentals is $10 + 7 + 2 + 1 = 20$.
$$\text{Drama} = 10 \div 20$$
$$= 0.5$$

$$\text{Comedy} = 7 \div 20$$
$$= 0.35$$

NOTES

Circle graphs are also known as pie charts.

$$\text{Action} = 2 \div 20$$
$$= 0.1$$

$$\text{Horror} = 1 \div 20$$
$$= 0.05$$

The total decimal numbers should add up to 1.
$$0.5 + 0.35 + 0.1 + 0.05 = 1$$

Step 2
Calculate each decimal number as an angle in degrees.
Multiply each decimal number by 360°.

$$\text{Drama} = 0.5 \times 360°$$
$$= 180°$$

$$\text{Comedy} = 0.35 \times 360°$$
$$= 126°$$

$$\text{Action} = 0.1 \times 360°$$
$$= 36°$$

$$\text{Horror} = 0.05 \times 360°$$
$$= 18°$$

Step 3
Draw a circle.
Use a compass to make a circle large enough to label the sectors.

Use a protractor to draw each of the angles or sectors. Start at the top of the circle graph, using the largest angle. Move in a clockwise direction until the smallest angle is drawn.

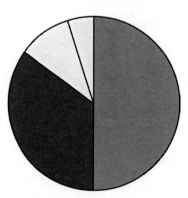

Step 4
Label the circle graph.
Include the category and percentage for each sector. Give the graph
a title.

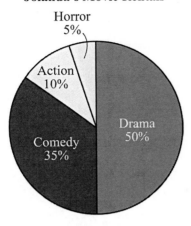

Jolanda's Movie Rentals

INTERPRETING CIRCLE GRAPHS

When you read and interpret a circle graph, you are analyzing the
information presented to answer questions about the data. Often, the
questions ask you to compare one category to another. However, you
cannot perform mathematical operations using percentages. They must be
converted into whole numbers first, and then the analysis can take place.

Example

Mariah surveyed the 20 students in her class who own pets to determine
the type of pet that each student has. She displayed her information in this
circle graph.

Family Pets in Class 7B

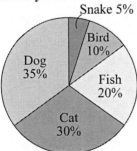

Use the circle graph to calculate how many students had each of the pets.

Solution
Step 1
Calculate each percentage as a decimal number.
Divide the percentage by 100.

$$Dog = 35 \div 100$$
$$= 0.35$$

$$Cat = 30 \div 100$$
$$= 0.30$$

$$Fish = 20 \div 100$$
$$= 0.20$$

$$Bird = 10 \div 100$$
$$= 0.10$$

$$Snake = 5 \div 100$$
$$= 0.05$$

Step 2
Multiply the decimal number by the total quantity.
$$Dog = 0.35 \times 20$$
$$= 7$$

$$Cat = 0.30 \times 20$$
$$= 6$$
$$Fish = 0.20 \times 20$$
$$= 4$$

$$Bird = 0.10 \times 20$$
$$= 2$$

$$Snake = 0.05 \times 20$$
$$= 1$$

To verify the calculations were done correctly, add up the number of students. It should equal a total quantity of 20.
$$7 + 6 + 4 + 2 + 1 = 20$$

REVIEW SUMMARY

- The perimeter of a circle is known as the circumference of a circle.
- Circumference is calculated by using the formula $C = \pi d$ or $C = 2\pi r$, where d represents the diameter of the circle and r represents the radius of the circle. The formula can be rearranged to solve for diameter $\left(d = \dfrac{C}{\pi}\right)$ or radius $\left(r = \dfrac{C}{2\pi}\right)$.
- Pi (π) is a mathematical constant found by dividing the circumference of any circle by its diameter.
  Pi is often shortened to 3.14 for ease of calculations, but is actually a non-repeating, non-terminating decimal number.
- Circle graphs display data in sections called sectors.

AREA

When you are finished this unit, you will be able to...

• use measurement to determine relationships between diameter, radius, and circumference of circles, and between base and height of parallelograms and triangles
• calculate the area of parallelograms, triangles, and circles
• solve problems involving the area of parallelograms, triangles, and circles

PREREQUISITE SKILLS AND KNOWLEDGE

Prior to starting this unit, you should be able to...

• convert between different metric units of measurement
• calculate the perimeter and area of rectangles

Lesson 1   AREA OF A PARALLELOGRAM

The area of a parallelogram can be found by transforming the parallelogram into a rectangle. To transform it, slide a triangular section of the parallelogram as shown in the following diagram.

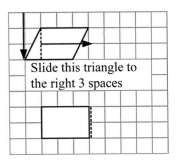

Slide this triangle to the right 3 spaces

A rectangle is a special parallelogram. Opposite sides are equal and opposite angles are equal.

The rectangle is 2 units high and 3 units long, so its area is 6 square units.

The base of the parallelogram is 3 units and the height is 2 units.

The area of the parallelogram is equal to the area of the rectangle.

Therefore, the area of the parallelogram is also 6 square units.

To find the area of a parallelogram, multiply the base by the height. $A = b \times h,$ where b represents the base and h represents the height.

To find the area of a parallelogram use the following steps:
Step 1
Determine the given measurements

Step 2
Apply the area formula, substitute the values in, solve.

Example
A parallelogram has a base that is 6.75 cm long and a height that is 5 cm. Calculate the area of the parallelogram.

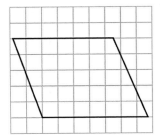

Solution
Step 1
Determine the given values. The base is 6.75 cm and the height is 5 cm.

Step 2
Apply the area formula, substitute in the given values and solve.
$A = b \times h$
$ = 6.75 \times 5$
$ = 33.75 \text{ cm}^2$

The area of the parallelogram is 33.75 cm².

When given the area of a parallelogram, you can find the value of a missing measurement by substituting the values you do know into the area formula.

Example

A parallelogram has a base that is 17.3 m long and an area of 95.15 m². Find the height of the given parallelogram.

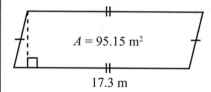

$A = 95.15 \text{ m}^2$

17.3 m

Solution

Step 1
Determine the given values. The base is 17.3 m and the area is 95.15 m².

Step 2
Apply the area formula, substitute in the given values and solve.
$$A = b \times h$$
$$(95.15) = (17.3) \times h$$
$$\frac{95.15}{17.3} = \frac{17.3h}{17.3}$$
$$5.5 = h$$

The height of the parallelogram is 5.5 m.

Lesson 2   AREA OF A TRIANGLE

The area of a triangle uses the same principles applied to finding the area of a rectangle.

Start with the formula used to find the area of a rectangle, which is $A = b \times h$.

Then cut the rectangle in half by drawing a line between opposite vertices. This cut produces two identical triangles.

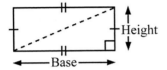

Since the area of a triangle is equal to half the area of a rectangle, the formula to calculate the area of a triangle is $A = \frac{1}{2}bh$.

Example

Calculate the area of one of the triangles in the given diagram.

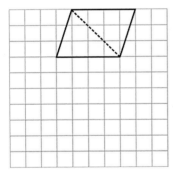

Solution

Step 1

Determine the given values.

The base is 4 square units and the height is 3 square units.

Step 2

Apply the area formula, substitute in the given values, and solve.

$$A = \frac{1}{2}bh$$
$$= \frac{4 \times 3}{2}$$
$$= \frac{12}{2}$$
$$= 6 \text{ units}^2$$

The area of each of the triangles is 6 square units.

When looking at diagrams of triangles, the height of the triangle is indicated with a line that goes from the top of the triangle to its base. It will form a right angle with the base.

In the following example, the base is extended with a dotted line to show where it would meet and form the right angle. Do not include the extended part in the area calculation, just the given length of the base.

Example

Calculate the area of the given triangle.

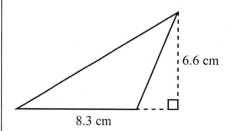

6.6 cm

8.3 cm

Solution

Step 1
Determine the given values.
The base is 8.3 cm and the height is 6.6 cm.

Step 2
Apply the area formula, substitute in the given values, and solve for the area.

$$A = \frac{1}{2}bh$$
$$= \frac{(8.3) \times (6.6)}{2}$$
$$= \frac{54.78}{2}$$
$$= 27.39 \text{ cm}^2$$

The area of the obtuse triangle is 27.39 cm².

The height of a triangle is the distance between the base and the vertex opposite.

The base and height of a triangle must be perpendicular to each other.

Lesson 3 AREA OF A CIRCLE

The area of a circle also uses the principles applied to finding the area of a rectangle.

If the circle is cut into equal sections, the pieces can be arranged to form a parallelogram with the following characteristics:
- The radius of the circle is equal to the height of the parallelogram.
- Half the circumference of the circle is equal to the base of the parallelogram.

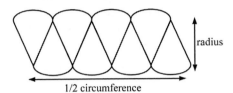

radius

1/2 circumference

Therefore,

$$A_{circle} = A_{parallelogram} \qquad A_{circle} = base \times height$$

$$A_{circle} = \frac{1}{2} circumference \times radius$$

$$A_{circle} = \frac{1}{2}(2\pi r) \times r \qquad A_{circle} = \frac{2\pi r}{2} \times r$$

$$A_{circle} = \pi \times r \times r \qquad A_{circle} = \pi r^2$$

The formula used to calculate the area of a circle is $A = \pi r^2$.

Use 3.14 in place of π when calculating the area of a circle. Using 3.14 approximates the answers.

Example
Calculate the area of the given circle.

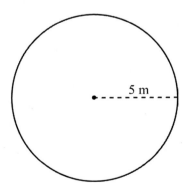

5 m

Solution
Step 1
Determine the given values.
The radius is 5 m.

$$base = \frac{1}{2} Circumference$$
$$= \frac{1}{2}(2\pi r)$$
$$height = radius$$
$$= r$$

Step 2
Apply the area formula, substitute in the given values, and solve.
$$A = \pi r^2$$
$$= (3.14)(5)^2$$
$$= (3.14)(25)$$
$$= 78.5 \text{ m}^2$$

The area of the circle is about 78.5 m².

If you are given the area of a circle and asked to find the missing radius, substitute in the values you are given and solve for the radius.

Example

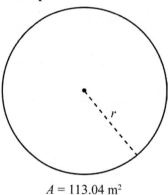

$A = 113.04$ m²

Calculate the radius of the given circle.

Solution
Step 1
Determine the given values.
The area is 113.04 m².

Step 2
Apply the area formula, substitute in the given values, and solve for the radius.
$$A = \pi r^2$$
$$113.04 = (3.14)r^2$$
$$\frac{113.04}{3.14} = \frac{3.14r^2}{3.14}$$
$$36 = r^2$$

The opposite of something squared is the square root. So take the square root of both sides to solve for r.
$$\sqrt{36} = \sqrt{r^2}$$
$$6 = r$$

The radius of the circle is 6 m.

REVIEW SUMMARY

- To calculate the area of any 2-D shape, use the given formulas for area, substitute in the known values, and solve. The units for area are always expressed in squared units.

- The area of a parallelogram can be found by transforming the parallelogram into a rectangle.
  The area formula for a parallelogram is $A = b \times h$.

- The area of a triangle is half the area of a rectangle. Therefore, the area formula for a triangle is $A = \dfrac{1}{2}bh$.

- The area of a circle uses the principles applied to finding the area of a parallelogram and can be found by using the formula $A = \pi r^2$.

- Other missing measurements can be found by substituting the given values into the appropriate area formulas, and solving for the unknown measurement.

PROBABILITY

When you are finished this unit, you will be able to…

- provide an example of an event with a probability of 0 or 0% (impossible) and an example of an event with a probability of 1 or 100% (certain)
- determine the probability of a given outcome occurring for a given probability experiment, and express it as a ratio, fraction, and percentage
- provide an example of two independent events and explain why they are independent
- identify the sample space for each of two independent events, using a tree diagram, table, or other graphic organizer
- determine the theoretical probability of a given outcome involving two independent events
- solve a given probability problem involving two independent events
- conduct a probability experiment for an outcome involving two independent events and compare the experimental probability with the theoretical probability

PREREQUISITE SKILLS AND KNOWLEDGE

Prior to beginning this unit, you should be able to…

- list possible outcomes for a single event.
- find the probability for single events.
- compare outcomes as equally likely, more likely, or less likely to occur.
- demonstrate that different outcomes may occur when repeating the same experiment.

Lesson 1 *INTRODUCTION TO PROBABILITY*

Probability is a measure of how likely it is for an event to occur.

An event with a probability of 0 means that event is impossible and will never happen. For instance, humans will never walk to the moon. The probability of that event is 0.

An event with a probability of 1 means that event is certain and will always happen. For instance, the sun will always rise in the east. The probability of that event occurring is 1.

The probability of everything else falls in between 0 and 1.

Example

Sophie goes to the candy store and purchases 5 red sour candies, 10 red liquorice candies, 5 red dolphin candies, and 10 red cola candies. The cashier puts all of her candies in a bag for her.

a) What is the probability of Sophie picking a red candy out of the bag?

Solution

All of the candies that Sophie purchased are red. Therefore, the probability of Sophie picking a red candy out of the bag is 1.

b) What is the probability of Sophie picking a blue dolphin candy out of the bag?

Solution

None of the candies that Sophie purchased are blue dolphin candies. Therefore, the probability of Sophie picking a blue dolphin candy out of the bag is 0.

Probability is the ratio of favourable outcomes to the total possible outcomes. The following formula can be used to calculate the probability of any given event:

$$P = \frac{\text{favourable outcome}}{\text{total possible outcomes}}$$

When determining the probability of a given experiment, substitute the known values into the probability formula and evaluate for the probability, *P*.

Probability can be expressed as a fraction, ratio, or a percentage.

Example

In a jar of jellybeans, there are 6 red jellybeans, 8 green jellybeans, and 10 yellow jellybeans.

What is the probability of picking a red jellybean out of the jar without looking?

Solution

Determine the number of favourable outcomes and total possible outcomes, substitute them into the probability formula, and evaluate for *P*.

$$P = \frac{\text{favourable outcome}}{\text{total possible outcomes}}$$

$$P(\text{red jellybean}) = \frac{6}{24}$$

$$= \frac{1}{4}$$

The probability of picking a red jellybean from the jar, expressed in fraction form is $\frac{1}{4}$.

The ratio can be expressed as *a*:*b*, where *a* represents the numerator and *b* represents the denominator. In this case, the ratio that compares the probability of picking a red jellybean from all the jellybeans in the jar is 1:4.

To express the fraction as a percentage, divide the numerator by the denominator and multiply the result by 100.

$$\frac{1}{4}$$

$$= 0.25 \times 100$$

$$= 25\%$$

There is a 25% chance of picking a red jellybean from the jar.

Lesson 2 INDEPENDENT EVENTS AND SAMPLE SPACE

Independent events are events in which the occurrence of one event has no effect on the occurrence of another event.

An example of independent events would be the tossing of two coins. The first coin could have the outcome of heads or tails, and the second coin could have the same outcome of heads or tails. The outcome of the first event has no effect on the second event.

To identify all the possible outcomes of two or more independent events, follow these steps:
1. Identify all possible outcomes of the first event.
2. Identify all possible outcomes of the second event as they pertain to each outcome in the first event.
3. Organize the outcomes in a table or a tree diagram.

When all the possible combinations are listed, you have identified the **sample space.**

Sample space is a data set that contains all possible outcomes of a probability experiment that involves two or more independent events.

Each outcome in the sample space is expressed as an ordered pair, and the entire sample space is enclosed in a set of curly brackets, such as { }.

Example

Glynn has a four-sided die and a spinner with the colours red, blue, green, and yellow distributed in equal sections.

Draw a table and tree diagram to identify all the possible outcomes. Then determine the sample space.

Solution
Step 1
Identify the outcomes of the first event.
Outcomes of rolling the die are: 1, 2, 3, 4.

Step 2
Identify the outcomes of the second event.
Outcomes of spinning the spinner are: Red, Blue, Green, Yellow.

Step 3

Organize the outcomes in a table or a tree diagram.

Use a table:
The table headers are the events in the experiment. Combine the outcome on the side of the table with the outcome at the top of the table.

Spinner

		Red (R)	Blue (B)	Green (G)	Yellow (Y)
	1	1R	1B	1G	1Y
Die	2	2R	2B	2G	2Y
	3	3R	3B	3G	3Y
	4	4R	4B	4G	4Y

Use a Tree Diagram:
Start with the first event (die), and list the outcomes (1, 2, 3, 4).
Draw a branch from each of these outcomes to each of the outcomes (red, blue, green, yellow) of the second event.

Roll	Spin	Possible outcomes
1	Red Blue Green Yellow	1R 1B 1G 1Y
2	Red Blue Green Yellow	2R 2B 2G 2Y
3	Red Blue Green Yellow	3R 3B 3G 3Y
4	Red Blue Green Yellow	4R 4B 4G 4Y

The sample space according to the table and the tree diagram is
{1R, 1B, 1G, 1Y, 2R, 2B, 2G, 2Y, 3R, 3B, 3G, 3Y, 4R, 4B, 4G, 4Y}.

Lesson 3 *THEORETICAL PROBABILITY VS. EXPERIMENTAL PROBABILITY*

There are two types of probability: theoretical probability and experimental probability.

Theoretical probability is the probability of an event occurring, and it is calculated mathematically. It is the number of favourable outcomes compared to the total number of possible outcomes.

Experimental probability is determined by actually conducting an experiment and using those results to calculate the probability.

Both theoretical probability and experimental probability are calculated using the probability formula:

$$P = \frac{\text{favourable outcome}}{\text{total possible outcomes}}$$

For example, when a coin is tossed, it is equally likely to obtain either heads or tails; therefore, the theoretical probability of the coin landing on heads is $\frac{1}{2}$. When the experiment is actually performed, heads might be obtained 3 times out of 4; thus, the experimental probability of the coin landing on a head is $\frac{3}{4}$.

When calculating experimental probability use the results of the experiment to identify the favourable outcomes and the total possible outcomes.

Calculate the probability of two independent events, follow these steps:

Step 1
Use a table or a tree diagram to determine the sample space.

Step 2
Calculate the probability by applying the probability formula.

Example

What is the probability of tossing heads on a coin and rolling a 4 on a regular number cube? Express the probability as a fraction.

Solution

Step 1

Determine the sample space using a table or tree diagram.

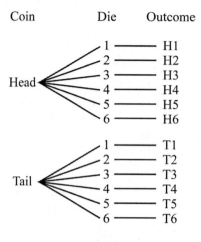

Step 2

Calculate the probability.

There are 12 possible outcomes and 1 favourable outcome.

$$P = \frac{\text{favourable outcome}}{\text{total possible outcomes}}$$

$$P(\text{H4}) = \frac{1}{12}$$

The probability of tossing heads and rolling a 4 is $\frac{1}{12}$.

Experimental probability is the likelihood of an event occurring when a trial is conducted. With experimental probability, a different outcome is possible each time the experiment is conducted.

The theoretical probability of two independent events and the experimental probability of two independent events need not always be the same.

However, as the number of trials in the experiment increases, the experimental probability will come closer and closer to the theoretical probability.

Example

A four-sided die is rolled 24 times and a spinner, coloured Red, Orange, and Yellow, is spun 24 times. The outcomes are recorded in the given table.

Outcomes	R1	R2	R3	R4	O1	O2	O3	O4	Y1	Y2	Y3	Y4
Frequency	1	2	0	2	3	4	4	2	1	3	1	1

Calculate the experimental probability of rolling a 3 on the four-sided die and spinning an orange on the spinner. Compare these results with the theoretical probability of rolling a 3 on the four-sided die and spinning orange on the spinner. Express the probabilities as percentages.

Solution

Step 1
Calculate the theoretical probability.
There are 24 possible outcomes and 4 favourable outcomes.

$$P = \frac{\text{favourable outcome}}{\text{total possible outcomes}}$$

$$P(O3) = \frac{4}{24}$$

$$= \frac{1}{6}$$

$$\doteq 17\%$$

Step 2
Calculate the experimental probability, using the outcomes in the given table. There are 12 possible outcomes and 1 favourable outcome.

$$P = \frac{\text{favourable outcome}}{\text{total possible outcomes}}$$

$$P(O4) = \frac{1}{12}$$

$$\doteq 8\%$$

The theoretical probability of rolling a 3 and spinning orange is much higher than its experimental probability.

The total possible outcomes in experimental probability is the number of times the experiment is carried out.

REVIEW SUMMARY

NOTES

- Probability is a measure of how likely it is for an event to occur. It is expressed as a number between 0 and 1.
- Outcomes are the possible results of conducting a probability experiment. Outcomes can be impossible, certain, or somewhere in between.
- Theoretical probability is the probability of an event occurring, and it is calculated mathematically using a formula.
- Experimental probability is determined by actually conducting a probability experiment and using the results of the experiment to calculate the probability.
- Both theoretical probability and experimental probability are calculated using the probability formula:

$$P = \frac{\text{favourable outcome}}{\text{total possible outcomes}}$$

- Independent events are events in which the outcomes of one event do not affect the outcomes of another event.
- Sample space is a data set that contains all possible outcomes of an experiment. Sample space can be identified by using tables or tree diagrams.
- To calculate the probability of two independent events, following these steps:
  1. Use a table or a tree diagram to determine the sample space.
  2. Calculate the probability by applying the probability formula.

DATA ANALYSIS

When you are finished this unit, you will be able to…

- determine mean, median, and mode for a given set of data, and explain why these values may be the same or different
- determine the range for a given set of data
- provide a context in which the mean, median, or mode is the most appropriate measure of central tendency to use when reporting findings
- solve a given problem involving the measures of central tendency
- explain the effect of outliers on the measures of central tendency for a given data set
- identify outliers in a given set of data, and justify whether or not they are to be included in reporting the measures of central tendency

PREREQUISITE SKILLS AND KNOWLEDGE

Prior to starting this unit, you should be able to…

- draw conclusions from a set of data
- describe the distribution of a set of data using the smallest and largest values, value in the middle, and frequency
- make comparisons between sets of data
- read and understand graphs

Lesson 1 MEASURES OF CENTRAL TENDENCY

When given a set of data, analysis can be performed to determine important information from the data. **Central tendency** is the tendency of data to merge around certain points near the middle of a set of data. The mean, median, and mode are three ways to measure central tendency for a set of data.

A **set of data** is an unordered collection of values. The set is usually within curly brackets { }.

MEAN
The **mean** is the average of all the values that make up a set of data.

To calculate the mean of a set of numbers, follow these steps:

Step 1
Find the sum of the values.

Step 2
Divide the total sum by the number of values.

Example
Calculate the mean of the data set {12, 10, 14, 8, 16}.

Solution
Step 1
Find the sum of the values.

$$12 + 10 + 14 + 8 + 16 = 60$$

Step 2
Divide the total sum by the number of values.

There are five values, so divide the sum by 5.
$$60 \div 5 = 12$$

The mean of the data set is 12.

MEDIAN
When the data is arranged in ascending order, the **median** is the middle value in a set of data. It divides the data so that 50% of the data is above the median and 50% is below the median.

There are two possibilities when calculating the median:
- An odd number of values in the data set—the number used is located exactly in the middle.
- An even number of values in the data set—the average of the two middle numbers is used.

166

To determine the median of a set of numbers, follow these steps:
Step 1
Place the values in ascending order.

Step 2
Determine the middle number or numbers.

Example

Determine the median of the data set {14, 18, 16, 12, 13, 17, 15}.

Solution
Step 1
Place the values in ascending order (least to greatest).
12, 13, 14, 15, 16, 17, 18

Step 2
Determine the middle number.

There are an odd number of values. Only one number is in the middle.
12, 13, 14, 15, 16, 17, 18

The median is 15.

Ascending order means ordering from smallest to largest

MODE
The mode of a set of data is the value that occurs most often.

There are three possibilities when calculating the mode:
• One mode—one number occurs more frequently than the other numbers.
• More than one mode—two or more numbers occur more than the other numbers and occur the same number of times.
• No mode—all the numbers occur the same number of times.

To determine the mode of a set of numbers, follow these steps:
Step 1
Place the values in ascending (least to greatest) order.

Step 2
Determine which numbers occur the most frequently, if any.

Example

Determine the mode of the data set {4, 9, 12, 7, 9, 2, 12, 8, 9, 4, 11, 3}.

Solution
Step 1
Place the values in ascending order.
2, 3, 4, 4, 7, 8, 9, 9, 9, 11, 12, 12

To remember the definition of mode, notice mode and most both start with the letters *mo*.

Step 2
Determine which number or numbers occur most frequently.
The numbers 4 and 12 occur twice, and 9 occurs three times. The rest of the numbers occur once.

The mode is 9 because it occurs more than any other number.

RANGE

Data is organized in increasing order to investigate the upper and lower extremes. From the extremes, the range can be calculated. **Range** is the difference between the highest and lowest values that make up a data set.

To find the range of a set of numbers, follow these steps:
Step 1
Place the numbers in ascending (least to greatest) order.

Step 2
Subtract the lowest value from the greatest value.

Example
18, 32, 12, 45, 23, 54, 33, 31, 35, 45, 30, 21
Find the upper and lower extremes and the range of the given data.

Solution
Step 1
Place the numbers in ascending order.

$$12, 18, 21, 23, 30, 31, 32, 33, 35, 45, 45, 54$$
$$\uparrow \qquad\qquad\qquad\qquad\qquad\qquad\qquad \uparrow$$

Lower extreme   Upper extreme

The smallest value is the lower extreme, and the largest value is the upper extreme. The range is the difference between the upper and lower extremes.

The lower extreme is 12, and the upper extreme is 54.

Step 2
Subtract the lowest value from the greatest value.

range = upper extreme − lower extreme
     $= 54 - 12 = 42$

Therefore, the upper extreme is 54, the lower extreme is 12, and the range is 42.

Lesson 2   USING MEASURES OF CENTRAL TENDENCY AND THE EFFECTS OF OUTLIERS

A value that is vastly different than the rest of the data is referred to as an **outlier**. This means that there is a great difference between an outlier and the closest value to it. Outliers can affect all measures of central tendency (mean, median, and mode), depending on the numbers in the data set.

A set of data has gaps if there are significant differences between data values. Clusters occur when there is a lot of data centered around one or more values.

The appropriate use of measures of central tendency to describe the data depends on the kind of data that is presented.

The mean is a good representation of central tendency for sets of data that have no major outliers. Because the mean is greatly affected by outliers, it is not a good representation for skewed data.

The median is a good representation of central tendency for data that contain outliers. Because the median is not greatly affected by outliers, it is a good representation for skewed data.

The mode is a good representation for central tendency for sets of categorical data. **Categorical data** is data that can be divided into groups. Examples of categorical data are size (small, medium, large), music style (pop, jazz, rock, hip hop), or age group (infant, toddler, adolescent, adult, senior).

To determine which measure of central tendency is affected by an outlier, follow these steps:

Step 1
Place the values in ascending (least to greatest) order.

Step 2
Determine the outlier.

Step 3
Calculate the mean, median, and mode with the outlier.

Step 4
Calculate the mean, median, and mode without the outlier.

Step 5
Compare the results of the calculations.

NOTES

Example

{10, 8, 21, 13, 8, 9, 10, 11, 12, 11, 8}

Identify which measure of central tendency is **most affected** when the outlier is removed.

Solution

Step 1

Place the values in ascending order.

8, 8, 8, 9, 10, 10, 11, 11, 12, 13, 21

Step 2

Determine the outlier.

The outlier in this set of data is 21 since the difference between it and 13 is the greatest.

Step 3

Calculate the mean, median, and mode with the outlier.

$$8 + 8 + 8 + 9 + 10 + 10 + 11 + 11 + 12 + 13 + 21 = 121$$
$$121 \div 11 = 11$$

The mean is 11.

The value 8 occurs three times, so the mode is 8.

8, 8, 8, 9, 10, $\boxed{10}$, 11, 11, 12, 13, 21

The median is 10.

Step 4

Calculate the mean, median, and mode without the outlier.

$$8 + 8 + 8 + 9 + 10 + 10 + 11 + 11 + 12 + 13 = 120$$
$$100 \div 10 = 10$$

The mean changes from 11 to 10.

There is an even number of values.

8, 8, 8, 9, $\boxed{10, 10}$, 11, 11, 12, 13

The average of the two middle values is 10, so the median is still 10.

8, 8, 8, 9, 10, 10, 11, 11, 12, 13

The value 8 occurs three times, so the mode is still 8.

Step 5

Compare the results of the calculations.

After removing the outlier, the mode is still 8, the median is still 10, and the mean changes from 11 to 10.

Removing the outlier affected the mean most.

Example

A golfer wants to know the best representation of his golf score.
The scores for 10 rounds of 18 holes of golf were collected and arranged in ascending order.

63, 63, 71, 73, 75, 79, 79, 83, 86, 88

Which measure of central tendency is **best** used in this situation?

Solution
Step 1
Assess the data.

Look for outliers and type of data.
There are no major outliers, so the data is not categorical.

Step 2
Choose the best measure of tendency.

The mean is a good option to use to describe the golf score since there are no outliers.

$$\frac{63 + 63 + 71 + 73 + 75 + 79 + 79 + 83 + 86 + 88}{10} = \frac{760}{10}$$
$$= 76$$

The golfer's average score is 76.

Mean is the best representation of his golf score using all the scores because there is no outlier.

Example

Evelyn works in a shoe store. She recorded the size of girls' shoes that were sold during the day.
6, 7, 6, 7, 7, 8, 7, 7, 9, 7, 7, 6, 6, 7

Which measure of central tendency is **best** used in this situation?

Solution
Step 1
Assess the data. Look for outliers and type of data. The data has no outliers. Shoes can be grouped into sizes, so the data is categorical.

Step 2
Choose the best measure of tendency. Mode is the best measure of central tendency for categorical data.

Place the values in ascending order: 6, 6, 6, 6, 7, 7, 7, 7, 7, 7, 7, 7, 8, 9

Size 7 shoes were the most popular size of shoe sold. Mode is the best representation of the shoe sizes sold because the data can be categorized.

REVIEW SUMMARY

- Measures of central tendency are measures of the centre of the data.
- The mean is the average of the data, and it is found by finding the sum of the data and dividing by the number of pieces of data.
- The mode is the most common number or numbers.
- The median is the middle number in a set of data organized in order from lowest in value to highest in value.
- The lower and upper extremes are the smallest and largest numbers, respectively.
- The range is the value that represents the difference between them.
- The lower and upper extremes of the data and the median are also used to separate the data into sections, each with 25% of the data.
- The outliers are values that are a great distance from the next closest value and can influence the measures of central tendency.

172

Credits

Every effort has been made to provide proper acknowledgement of the original source and to comply with copyright law. However, some attempts to establish original copyright ownership may have been unsuccessful. If copyright ownership can be identified, please notify Castle Rock Research Corp so that appropriate corrective action can be taken.

Some images in this document are from www.clipart.com, copyright (c) 2011 Jupiterimages Corporation.

NOTES